MOTORBOAT SYSTEMS

James Yates

Helmsman Books

First published in 1993 by
Helmsman Books, an imprint of
The Crowood Press Ltd
Ramsbury, Marlborough
Wiltshire SN8 2HR

British Library Cataloguing in Publication Data
A catalogue record for this book is available from the British Library.

ISBN 1 85223 762 7

Acknowledgements
The author would like to thank the following for their help and
assistance in providing information and photographs for this book:

Peter Caplen for photographs and descriptions of the Sea-Talk
navigation system he has fitted to his boat; Chris Cattrall for
photographs and technical information; Steve Hunt of Greenacre
Photographic; Bernard Martin of Lucas Rists Wiring Systems. Thanks
are also due to the many manufacturers who provided illustrations of
their products; their help is fully acknowledged and very much
appreciated.

Line-drawings by Claire Upsdale-Jones

Throughout this book, he, his and him have been used as neutral
pronouns and thus refer to both men and women.

Typeset by Avonset, Midsomer Norton, Bath.
Printed and bound in Great Britain by Redwood Books, Trowbridge.

CONTENTS

PREFACE

The advent of micro-electronics has changed the way in which the navigator guides his vessel. Not only does he have VHF radios, echo-sounders and speed logs – items that have been available for many years in one form or another – but he now also has radar, satellite navigation systems, the Decca navigation system and chart plotters to add to his ever-growing armament of navigation instruments.

Modern navigation systems are also becoming more and more interdependent, with the radar, automatic pilot and navigator all 'talking' to each other, using each others' data, and integrating with each other to provide the navigator with constantly updated information on course to steer, latitude and longitude position and fixes. All this wonderful equipment does not, however, absolve the competent helmsman and navigator from learning and practising his standard paper chart-work theory and techniques. If it did, where would he turn to if the electronics suddenly and inexplicably went down?

The object of this book is to give an insight into the various systems that go to make up a motor boat. Not only does it deal with the aforementioned electronic and navigation equipment, but it also covers communications, interference and radar systems. It examines how they work, what makes them tick and how they can be fitted to the average motor boat. Apart from the electronic side, other systems covered include the 'domestic' equipment aboard: toilets and plumbing; bilge pumps and water systems; the gas supply; and deck fittings. All are described fully and illustrated copiously with photographs and diagrams to help the boat owner decide which is best for his particular boat and how best to fit it once he has made his purchase. The text has been written assuming little or no previous knowledge and so will be suitable for the first-timer as well as the seasoned boat owner.

The buying and installation of boating equipment is part of the pleasure of owning and using a boat. The aim of this book is to bring together many years of knowledge in what I hope is an interesting and readable form. If you are considering fitting out a hull from scratch, refurbishing a second-hand boat or simply updating your present craft, the information contained here should help you through the maze of system types and, if you do decide to do it yourself, it might even save you some money!

1
ELECTRONIC
SYSTEMS

There are two schools of thought when it comes to the modern electronic equipment available for marine use today. The first is the traditional view which considers that using machines to make all the calculations involved in navigation takes away the challenge and fun of being afloat. This view can be taken to extremes by purists who prefer to use oil lamps and spirit stoves, and who really hate the idea of ever starting the engine. The other extreme is the view of the computer-age wizard who eagerly anticipates the next advance in microchip technology and

A comprehensive array of electronics. Left to right: Decca Navigator, chart plotter, radar, log, compass, autopilot, echo-sounder, VHF radio, fish-finder, Navtex and fuel computer.

who cannot wait to get it installed on his boat. Obviously the latter view is rather more costly than the first, but both have their merits. I suspect, however, that the majority of boat owners fall somewhere between these two schools of thought, and have plenty of brass fittings surrounding the electronic equipment.

The middle position is certainly my own, and I have always striven to fit the best of electronic equipment to my boat while still reading by the light of traditional-looking gimballed brass lamps. I enjoy the simple pleasures of mooring in a secluded anchorage and listening to the evening sounds of sea birds in the saltings, but I much prefer to get there simply by engaging the autopilot and letting the chart plotter do its work. Make no mistake, this does not make me any less of a seaman than the spartan traditionalist – in fact, I will probably

achieve greater navigational accuracy as I have additional free time to keep a proper look-out and check and update my position on the paper chart without having to worry about steering an accurate course.

Let me emphasize from the start that electronic charting does not replace the paper chart; it simply augments it. The most ardent electronic *aficionado* would be an idiot to leave port without an up-to-date paper chart of his cruising area, as even the finest of electronic equipment can fail as a result of lack of battery power – usually at the most inopportune moment. Electronics enhance cruising enjoyment by taking the drudgery out of navigation and almost always offer far greater accuracy than even the most astute navigator. There are enough problems to be encountered at sea, and anything that eases the work-load is fine by me.

A boating friend of mine has just

Sea-Talk waterproof helm instruments. Left to right: speed/depth repeater, steering compass, ST6000 autopilot control, Navdata console (satnav, GPS or Decca navigator repeater).

installed a complete set of Sea-Talk equipment from Nautech, the makers of the world-renowned Autohelm autopilots. As this system demonstrates electronic integration between radar, autopilot, chart plotter, echo-sounder, speed log and compass, it seems an excellent example of how complete a small boat electronic navigation system can be. I shall therefore describe its operation and installation below, before going on to look at specialist systems such as Decca, satnav and GPS.

The Sea-Talk System

Installation

Although each instrument in the Sea-Talk system passes information through to a central 'Navcenter', this does not mean that there is a vast wiring loom to be installed. In fact, quite the opposite is true as each instrument has just two plugged cables and one socket to connect. The socket is for the transducer cable plug, while the two cables (consisting of a three-core cable each) do everything else. Two of these three cores are for battery power (positive and negative), while all information between instruments is passed down the third single core. Connection is therefore very simple, consisting of plug-together connections which allow instruments to be connected in series and cable runs to be hidden neatly.

The item which requires the most care in installation is the autopilot, and if the installation is performed by the owner

State-of-the-art log and echo-sounders from Nautech. Part of their Sea-Talk range, the instruments can be integrated fully with an autopilot, satellite navigator and Decca receiver. The instrument to the right is a combination of the two on the left.

then Nautech insist on having it checked and tested by one of their agents before validating the guarantee. However, if the instructions are followed and the specifications for cable sizes and hydraulic pipework are adhered to, there is no reason why the installation should not be as good as or better than a professional job.

Installing any autopilot needs care and attention to detail, especially when arranging the mounting for the rudder drive. This may be a hydraulic pump and ram, a linear motor, or a rotary drive. The thrust to turn the rudder can be very considerable in rough weather and if the drive mountings are not up to the job they will soon fail and leave the boat with jammed steering. It is therefore essential to build the mountings as strongly as possible. On glass-reinforced plastic (GRP) vessels the shelf needs to be bonded in, as do adequate strengtheners. On wooden vessels a framework of similar strength to the engine beds is needed.

Autopilot Computer

The computer unit for the autopilot is not watertight and must therefore be mounted in a dry, protected position. Once it is fitted no maintenance or adjustments are required, so it can be placed well out of harm's way. The installation specifications call for a maximum cable run between the computer and rudder motor to prevent voltage drop degrading steering performance. The cable size is also important and depends on the length of run. The control units can be fitted in any convenient position near the helm.

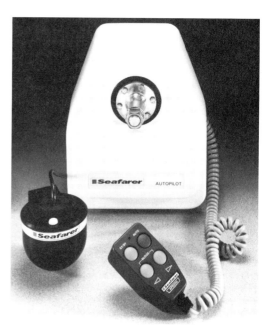

The heading display from Nautech's Sea-Talk autopilot. The reading is large enough to be seen from a distance and is illuminated at night. It can also be integrated fully with other electronics such as the radar.

An unusual autopilot, this AP500 from Seafarer is fitted behind the steering wheel of the motor boat. The direction sensor is installed elsewhere in the boat and remote control is available via a push-button on a lead.

Electronics have advanced into the field of compasses, reflected in the many types of fluxgate models available like this popular Voyager unit from Seafarer.

The final piece of autopilot hardware to fit is the fluxgate compass which includes auto-calibration. All that is required is to find an area on board which is fairly free of magnetic fields, then fit the compass so that it faces towards the bow and is accurately aligned fore and aft. It is best to mount the compass as low in the boat as possible to give the steadiest readings in all sea conditions.

Once the autopilot has been set up, installing the rest of the equipment is no different from that of any other make. The depth-meter transducer must be installed in an area free from turbulence caused by keels or fins, while the paddle-wheel speed transducer also needs a clean flow of water to give a steady and accurate reading. In a GRP craft the depth trans-ducer will function when mounted inside the hull, but on steel or wooden craft it must be mounted through the hull.

The layout of the instruments them-selves is entirely up to the owner's taste and the style of the control panel. How-ever, as all the Sea-Talk instruments are very slim, with a depth of less than 2.5cm (1in), it is possible to face-mount most of them without spoiling the look of the panels. Face-mounting the instruments is simplified by using the supplied cutting templates to drill accurately the clearance holes required for the back of the instru-ments. These templates have self-adhesive backs and can therefore be accurately positioned and spaced before you actually start cutting into the panels.

A Fully Integrated System

The brain and muscles of the system are the Navcenter, chart plotter and the auto-pilot, while the sensory functions are performed by the speed log, compass and (optional) NavData, translating infor-mation from a position fixer such as Decca or GPS. My friend uses a Navstar 2000D which can only input data to the Navcenter via the decoding facilities of the NavData repeater. When the system

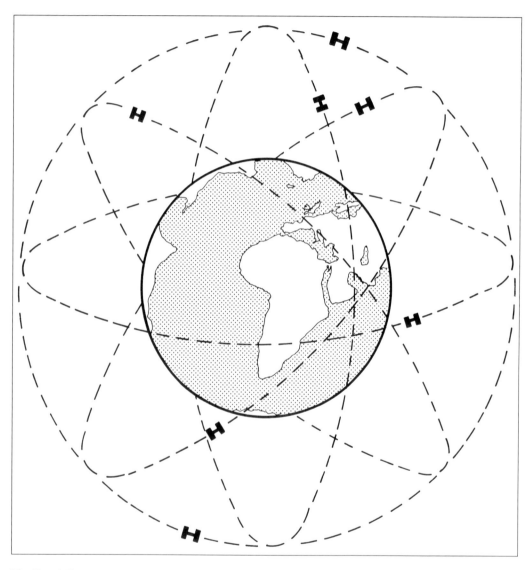

The Transit Satnav system comprises a ring of orbiting satellites at a height of around 660 miles. They travel from north to south then back to north again.

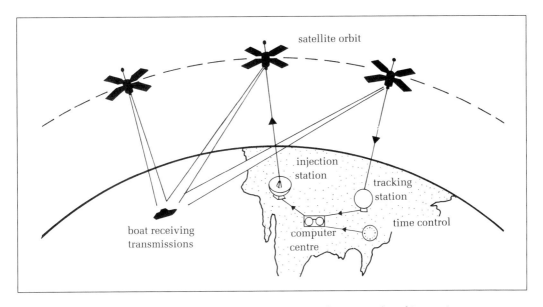

satellite orbit

injection station

tracking station

time control

boat receiving transmissions

computer centre

The Transit Satnav system needs up to six operational satellites, three ground tracking stations, a computing centre, its injection station and an observatory for time signals with which to synchronize the network.

was first put on sale this was not generally realized, and owners of the Navstar 2000D found that they had to buy the NavData to allow communication between systems. As my friend has a dual station set-up this was not a problem as he needed the repeater facility anyway, although his Navstar Decca had to be returned to the manufacturer for a low-cost modification to bring it up to the latest specification before he could actually get the two systems to cohabit satisfactorily.

Although the Sea-Talk is a very sophisticated system, with navigational computing power greater than that found on many ships, it is also very flexible, with each instrument functioning perfectly well as a stand-alone. For the average owner struggling on a tight budget this means that each item can be purchased separately and fully utilized until such time as funds permit further purchases.

Planning the System

Obviously there is a need to plan ahead which items will be purchased and in what order. I would suggest that the one item of modern electronic equipment that has the most impact on boating enjoyment is the autopilot. If you have never sampled the delights of cruising with an autopilot you will not believe the difference it can make to the enjoyment of long passages in difficult sea conditions. You suddenly find that there is time to study the chart and make leisurely calculations without having to worry that the helmsman is losing concentration and deviating off course – all that is needed is to appoint someone as watchkeeper while you are below with the charts.

Chart Plotter

Once the autopilot is installed, the chart plotter provides the next quantum leap into the future of electronic navigation by taking control of the actual track of the vessel and removing the need for constantly updating tidal information manually. Once again, however, I must stress the importance of keeping a full logged record of all navigational information as back-up against battery or equipment failure. That said, the time taken to maintain a back-up log is far less than actually performing all the computations manually. For most skippers who have grown up with navigation as the primary chore on board, the thought of leaving all calculations to a computer-based unit may be a little nerve-racking. My friend has therefore developed a simple system which utilizes both the chart plotter and manual calculations for initial passage planning, with regular position fixes during the voyage.

The Navcenter chart plotter collates all the information fed to it from the other equipment and, having digested the information, instructs the autopilot on which course to steer. The most noticeable difference between steering with a manually set autopilot and one being driven via a plotter is that the course on the manually set pilot remains constant until the helmsman inputs another course. With the plotter-driven pilot the course is updated constantly to account for the changes in wind and tide direction and strength. This provides an exact track-following course which would be very time-consuming to plot manually. The normal track-following method for manual navigation is to alter course each hour, this still giving a certain leeway off

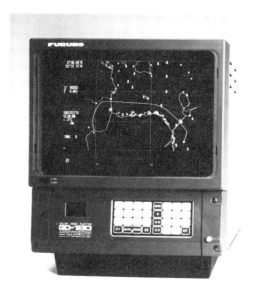

An electronic chart plotter which displays an electronic chart on a colour video screen. The various charts are stored on special cartridges and are changed as required. Many chart plotters can now be interfaced with other navigation instruments such as a satellite navigator.

course between hourly alterations. The chart plotter automatically updates the course to account for changes in conditions from minute to minute. Should a battery or equipment failure occur while on passage, the manually kept log allows the navigator to take control immediately as he knows exactly where the vessel is at the time.

The electronic charts for the plotter are supplied on separate cartridges by C-Map, the standard supplier for all makes of chart plotter. These can be purchased to suit the cruising area of the boat, although a large-scale chart covering Europe and America is included with the plotter. This is sufficiently detailed to allow courses to be put in from place to place for autopilot track controlling without the need to purchase further chart cartridges. Used in this way, with up-to-date paper charts for detailed plotting, there are no additional costs. However, most people do buy cartridges of their local area as they offer a great deal more detail than the large-scale internal chart, and these can be updated by C-Map as new editions are produced.

Moving about on the screen is performed using the track ball, which is mounted towards the top of the front of the control panel. This moves a cross-hair cursor across the screen in any direction, thereby allowing precise positioning of waypoints when on maximum zoom.

The data panel to the right of the screen shows a lot of information displayed for the navigator's use. At the top is the cursor position in latitude and longitude, and immediately below this is the course and speed over the ground. Next down is the distance and bearing of the cursor from the vessel's position when a position-fixer such as Decca or GPS is in use. Below this is the scale for the current zoom mode and the time is also constantly displayed. Below the time is the note-pad area which displays details of the names and characteristics of buoys on which the cursor is positioned, and other details such as places of interest inserted by the navigator.

To steer with the compass, the vessel is turned on to the course and the lock-button is pressed. This sets the course into the memory and the swing of the needle shows the amount by which the vessel is off course. It is a particularly easy format by which to steer as the direction needed to alter back on to the correct course is intuitive. The vessel is steered in the direction that the needle must move to return to zero.

The autopilot is in 'auto' mode and will

display the same magnetic course as the compass – hardly surprising as both are driven from the same fluxgate compass. Once in track control under the influence of the Navcenter, the display alters to indicate that track mode is selected. The display on the NavData indicates course and speed over the ground and is repeated from the Navcenter.

Using the System

Like most boat owners who have been brought up on traditional methods of navigation, I find the thought of leaving the navigation entirely in the hands of an electronic gizmo somewhat worrying to say the least. I know that there are owners of large sea-going craft who rely entirely on their electronics to get them home, but these foolhardy types have generally come into boating late in life and do not want to be bothered with the complexities of learning new skills. For the rest of us there is a great deal of comfort to be gleaned from having an up-to-date chart on the table filled with the passage plan for the day or even several days. I could never be without this comfort even though I have great faith in the reliability of my Sea-Talk equipment.

For the example above, I have assumed that the plotter is used in conjunction with a position-fixer such as Decca or GPS since there is not much point in using one as a stand-alone because the detail available on a paper chart will be greater than that shown on the plotter and at a fraction of the price. As I keep emphasizing (and as Nautech also emphasize in their manual), a chart plotter is no substitute for paper charts and proper chartwork; it is a means of easing the chore of navigation while also

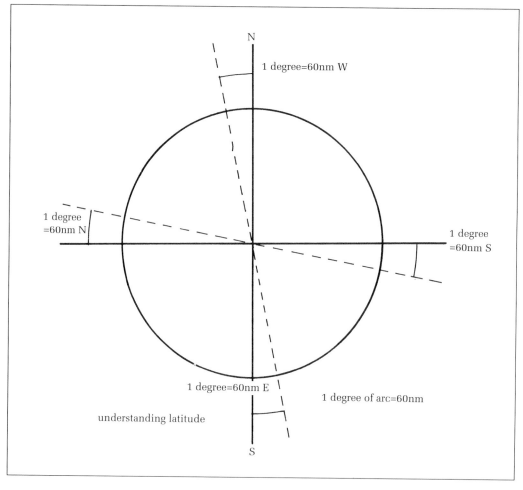

N

1 degree=60nm W

1 degree
=60nm N

1 degree
=60nm S

1 degree=60nm E

1 degree of arc=60nm

understanding latitude

S

To understand latitude, imagine a rigid pointer pivoted at the very centre of the Earth's globe and stretching out to the Equator. If you raise the point's tip 1 degree from the horizontal, it will have covered 60 miles. Equally, swinging it 1 degree east or west of the greenwich Meridian will cause it to pass through the same 60-mile angular distance.

taking the tiring stress out of steering when the track-control facility is controlling the autopilot.

My friend tells me that he would now not wish to be without his Sea-Talk set-up of Navcenter, chart plotter and ST6000 pilot. Together with his Decca they have made his cruising vastly more pleasurable.

The Decca Navigation System

The Decca navigation system has been in use for many years on commercial and large fishing vessels, but it is only relatively recently that the development of the silicon chip has made small units suitable for private pleasure craft and angling boats both possible and affordable.

The system was originally developed during the Second World War but was adopted rapidly by commercial shipping on the return of peace. As you would expect, the original equipment was extremely bulky and gave its position readouts in co-ordinates which had to be plotted on a special chart with a Decca grid overlay. A similar system was used up until a few years ago and is still in use today on many commercial ships. This system generally has a greater degree of accuracy, but the advent of the silicon chip has made it possible for the modern small-boat Decca receiver to convert the co-ordinates into latitude and longitude read-outs which are much simpler for the amateur skipper to use. It also means that the special overlay charts are no longer necessary as positions can be plotted directly on to a standard chart, thereby saving additional expense.

Chains

The Decca system is divided into chains of transmitters consisting of a master

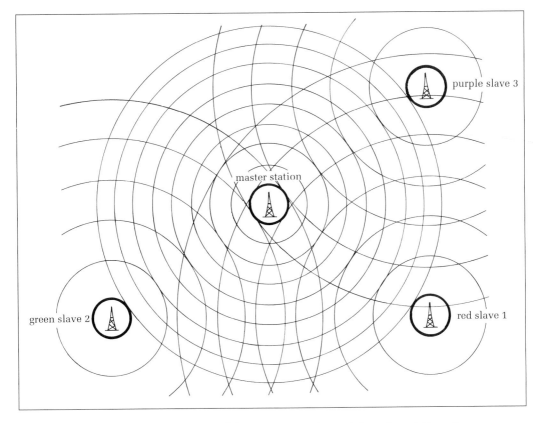

The Decca chain. The signals are transmitted from a master station and three slave stations. A position can be calculated each time two lines cross.

transmitter near the centre of the chain and either two or three slave transmitters placed between 50 and 150 miles away from the master. Each slave is identified by a colour code: slave 1 is red, slave 2 is green and slave 3 is purple. These colours were used with the original system of special overlay charts to assist with plotting the position from the co-ordinates displayed by the receiver.

Each transmitter sends out a signal which is received by the antenna of the on-board receiver, and when two signals of the same frequency are received from the master and one slave their phasing is compared. As each transmitter will have been in phase at the time of transmission the difference between the phasing of the two signals on reception gives a curved line of position (LOP). When further signals from the master and another slave are received and compared for phase, an additional line of position is calculated and the point where the two lines cross is the position of the boat. As with manual radio direction-finding there is always a varying degree of error on a fix from two positions, so where the chain includes a third slave the extra set of signals give a further line of position and therefore a much more accurate vessel position.

In practice, there is always a small degree of error involved in the displayed position, but this is usually only about 60m (65yd) in ideal conditions so for practical purposes it can be ignored. In less than ideal conditions such as at dawn or dusk, or during a winter's night, the accuracy will be much less and could be as much as 800m (½ mile). On the very edges of the transmission area covered by a chain this figure could rise to as much as 5km (3 miles) in the worst conditions, but the navigator should know that he is near the edge of the Decca area and will probably be using other methods of position-fixing to double-check.

Error Allowances

Happily, the modern Decca receivers give a read-out of received signal strength and an estimate of the expected accuracy for different conditions, so there is little chance of not allowing for errors in adverse conditions. In practice the Decca system gives the highest degree of accurate position-fixing for the British Isles and northern Europe in most conditions, over and above Satnav which suffers from gaps in satellite transmissions, and Loran which does not have the same degree of pinpoint accuracy. The Decca system is therefore the ideal position-fixing medium for the pleasure boat owner, with its high degree of accuracy in most conditions and relatively low price for the sophistication offered.

The most basic Decca model offers the minimum of facilities in favour of a rock-bottom price, with constantly updated position and manual chain selection. At the price it is a real bargain for the skipper who does not wish to make extended passages and who only requires position information. Slightly more sophisticated is the Navstar Dinghy-D which offers constantly updated position, auto-chain selection, a man-overboard facility which freezes the display when the appropriate button is pressed, and signal 'confidence' level which gives an indication of the accuracy of the displayed position. Cheapest and ostensibly the simplest to operate of the more sophisticated models is the Navstar 2000D which, as well as offering constantly updated position information, auto-chain selection and man-overboard facility, also includes waypoint navigation facilities for longer cruises.

Programming

All the aforementioned units need to be programmed initially with the vessel's (and therefore the receiver's) position to within 3km (2 miles) of the starting point. After this is entered the unit will continually update its position automatically and, with the exception of the cheapest unit, change chains as required. When switched off, an internal memory – usually powered by a rechargeable internal battery (automatically charged when the unit is operating) – keeps the last known position ready for when the unit is next used. It is essential always to switch the unit on before moving the boat to another position or the unit will require

the new position to be entered manually before use. It should also be noted that if this is not done the unit will continue to function – apparently normally – but the positions displayed will be incorrect in an amount equal to the distance from the unit's last known position to the position where it was switched on.

More expensive models like the latest AP navigators from Ampro, while having all the facilities offered by the previously mentioned models, also include auto-initialling whereby they automatically find the start position and switch on, and cannot therefore become 'lost'.

Transit Satnav

Satellite navigation has now been in existence for over twenty-five years, but it was the advent of the ubiquitous microchip and microprocessor technology that

The Navstar 2000 satellite navigator uses the Transit satnav system. It is shown here displaying latitude and longitude.

enabled receivers to be smaller, cheaper and more reliable, and – important to the small pleasure boat owner – to consume less power. The Transit Satnav system consists of up to six operational satellites, three ground tracking stations, a computing centre, two injection stations and a naval observatory for time signals.

Orbits

The satellites themselves are in near-circular polar orbits at a nominal height of around 666 miles (they travel from north to south and back to north again). The orbital planes of the satellites intersect at the Earth's axis of rotation. Each satellite is spaced from its neighbours in terms of the longitude of its plane of orbit. Ideally, the orbit planes should be spaced equally around the Earth, but in practice they vary slightly.

Satellites travel at around 14,000 knots and each completes a full orbit of the Earth in about 107 minutes. This means that they pass within lines of sight of an observer at least twice when he is near one of the orbits, and each satellite should provide at least four position fixes every twenty-four hours. A position fix may be obtained whenever one of the satellites rises above the observer's horizon to an acceptable altitude/elevation. For practical purposes, to obtain a satisfactory fix it is normally considered that the minimum and maximum satellite elevation should lie within the range 10–80 degrees.

As the satellites speed around their orbits, tracking stations receive their 150MHz and 400MHz signals, measure the Doppler frequency shift (caused by the satellite's motion) and record it as a function of time. This is then sent to the computing centre where the data is processed and future orbits of the satellites predicted with great accuracy.

Navigation Message

An injection station transmits a navigation message back to the satellites where details of their projected orbit for the next sixteen hours are stored in the satellites' memories. Each satellite receives a new navigation message from the injection stations roughly every twelve hours.

As a satellite travels around its orbit, it continually transmits its navigation message which lasts exactly two minutes. Each message consists of two parts: one fixed, containing the orbit parameters; and one variable, containing a set of corrections which are then added to the first part. Together these two parts define the precise position of the satellite at each two-minute time point. The latter portion is variable because every two minutes a new orbital correction is added and the oldest deleted. This keeps the navigation message fully up to date with the changes in the satellite's position.

The high velocity of the satellite produces a significant Doppler shift in the received 400MHz carrier frequency used by the single-frequency satnav receiver aboard the boat. The Doppler shift varies continuously during a satellite pass as the velocity of the satellite relative to the receiving antenna changes. Your satellite receiver measures this shift continuously by comparing the received frequency with a very accurate, internally generated reference frequency.

The general principle of satellite fixing is relatively simple. Your receiver simply measures the difference in slant range of the boat from a series of sequential positions of the satellite during its pass. This is done by counting the number of Doppler-shifted frequency cycles occurring between each of the two-minute timing marks. The Doppler shift phenomenon is simply the apparent change in the received frequency when the slant distance between the satellite is increasing or decreasing as a result of the combined orbital velocity of the satellite, the velocity of the boat and the rotation of the Earth about its axis.

Having received the minimum number of Doppler counts required by the receiver computer program, the chip uses the precise orbit information received (and temporarily stored in the computer memory), plus the boat's dead-reckoning position to calculate the slant range changes at each of the two-minute intervals. These are then compared with measured slant range changes and the dead-reckoning position is adjusted until these match.

Course and Speed

During the period of satellite pass it is important that your boat's course and speed should, if possible, remain constant. You will know the exact time of each satellite pass from orbital predictions available on your navigator display. As your boat will have moved a distance of some miles during the computing period, the input of accurate dead-reckoning information is essential. If you do not have automatic input, you must feed the latest course and speed into the receiver just prior to a satellite pass.

A modern satellite receiver will supply additional information to the navigator apart from just measurements of latitude and longitude. Many models will now

The Navstar 2000 aerial is small and can be mounted almost anywhere. In this photograph it is mounted on to a sea railing, although I would have preferred a higher position, perhaps on the cabin roof or on a short antenna mast.

show time, date, heading, speed, last satellite fix, future satellite alerts, and wind information on up to ten waypoints (including waypoint to waypoint calculation). Also available are audible alerts for waypoint approach, nearest point of approach and satellite fix obtainers.

Installation of Receivers

When choosing a Transit satellite receiver there are a number of alternatives. The cheapest receivers are single-channel units which require course and speed inputs to be inserted manually. The receivers in the middle of the range have the facility to input your course and speed automatically, and to combine this with waypoint navigation functions. It is always useful to get a receiver with as large a waypoint capacity as possible, as well as a memory capable of retaining them. In this way you will not have to go through the laborious task of inserting your co-ordinates each and every time you go to sea.

At the top of the range are the dual-channel receivers. The Transit satellites transmit on 150MHz and 400MHz, and by using these two frequencies the effects of refraction can be eliminated to give a higher degree of accuracy. Providing there is an accurate speed input, the errors of the fix can be halved by the use of a dual-channel receiver.

Installation of a satnav receiver is simple and the average boat owner should be capable of doing it himself. The antenna is small and compact and is easily mounted. Preferably, it should be installed in a position where it is not obstructed from an all-round view by, for example, part of the superstructure of the boat. A good earthing point is essential on the receiver as is a reliable power supply, but otherwise the installation is fairly strightforward.

More satellites have recently been launched into the network, which should improve the coverage and reduce the interval between fixes. They also have a stronger signal, although they are fully compatible with the existing satellites. Occasions can arise when more than one satellite is available for a position fix, but a modern receiver will automatically select the strongest signal.

Transit Satnav will still be with us at least until the end of the 1990s, so in-vestment in a new receiver is still a worthwhile proposition.

GPS System

The GPS or Global Positioning System is another satellite system, although more advanced in its technology than the Transit Satnav system. It is now fully operational around the globe and gives continuous, accurate fixes anywhere in the world. The system was partially operational, covering mainly the Atlantic and northern hemisphere, but with the advent of regular Space Shuttle flights a complete set of satellites has been deployed to give the global coverage we can use today. The cost of the GPS receivers has also come down considerably over the last three years or so, although they are still beyond the reach of some small-boat owners.

The system, as I have said, comprises a set of satellites, some eighteen in all, each of which rotates in a fixed orbit with an inclination of 55 degrees to the others. Each satellite takes twelve hours for one complete Earth orbit and they are arranged so that four satellites are above the horizon at any given time, regardless of your position in the world. The operating mode of GPS is similar to that of the Transit system, but because of the greater number of satellites used the position information is far more reliable and accurate.

Now that the full system is operational there has been plenty of time to assess possible errors, and remarkably few have been found – even on power boats used at speeds in excess of 45 knots. Prevailing weather conditions at the time of use have also been found to have little effect upon

This boat is fitted with a mast constructed from metal tubing. The VHF, satellite and Decca aerials have been mounted on it to make a neat installation.

This glass-fibre motor boat has an aerial mast fitted to the targa bow, or goal-post mast, to give the aerial height. The ball-shaped object is the sender for the fluxgate compass.

the accuracy of fixes, and neither have night operation or electrical storms. The system is also claimed to have an accuracy down to 30m (35yd)! The GPS system is expected to become more widely used than the Transit Satnav system and, as such, there will be plenty of receivers available on the market and increasingly competitive prices during the next few years.

Installing Electronics

Many other items of increasingly sophisticated electronic equipment are becoming available to the pleasure boat owner at prices within the reach of almost everybody, no matter how small their craft. Echo-sounders are probably the first item to be purchased when fitting out a boat, and these now offer a host of features which would have been unheard of a few years ago before the use of microchip technology to assist with clear displays and high levels of signal discrimination.

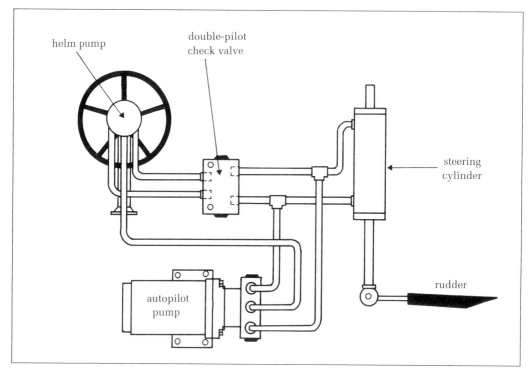

Schematic diagram of an autopilot system showing the hydraulic lines from wheel, valve and pump, all of which have a final bearing on the steering cylinder which is coupled to the rudder of the boat. (Courtesy of Nautech.)

Decca navigators can pinpoint a wreck's position to within a few hundred metres and simultaneously offer course and bearing information while on passage, again thanks to their inbuilt chips. Radar is similarly sophisticated, as are radio-telephones, and all these items have one thing in common in that they all send or receive radio or sound signals of one type or another. This can lead to mutual interference between equipment, resulting in poor performance which is not only annoying but also dangerous if erroneous information is being received (*see* Chapter 3).

Of all the items mentioned so far,

It is important when installing wiring, especially that for electronic devices to ensure that it is neat.

navigational equipment suffers most from interference from outside sources. However, as a precaution against the operator failing to realize that the information being displayed is incorrect, these items are generally self-checking and will give an alarm message when the signal is lost or degraded.

Power Supplies

When installing any electrical equipment it is essential to follow a few basic rules if satisfactory performance is to be obtained. The first and most important rule is to have separate batteries for the electronics and engine starting systems. This prevents the heavy discharge of the engine battery during starting from causing the electronics to shut down momentarily through low battery voltage. By having two batteries and a split charging system this problem is avoided from the outset. The electronics battery can then also be used for the on-board domestic supply and provides the added advantage that the engine can be restarted and domestic battery recharged if it is accidentally discharged by excess electrical consumption while at anchor. As the voltage is raised during charging the electronics will be usable more or less as soon as the engine is started.

Most electronic equipment installation instructions suggest that the positive lead should be connected directly to the

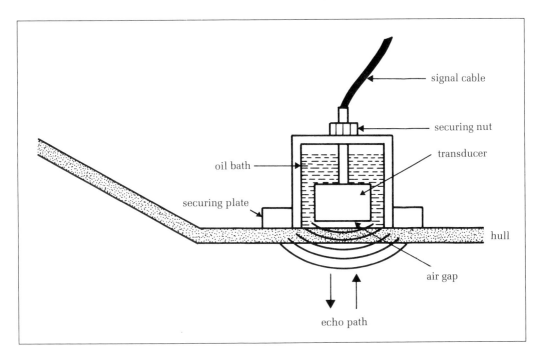

The transducer of an echo-sounder. A signal beam is transmitted from the transducer down into the water. The signal is reflected back from the sea-bed where the return signal is processed by the on-board computer in the sounder head. The difference in time between transmission and reception can be calculated and shown as depth on a visual display.

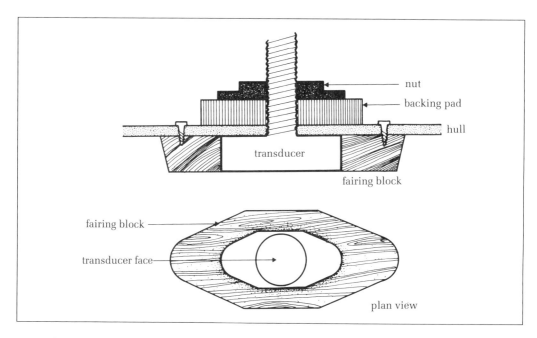

Fitting the transducer to the hull of the boat. The unit is usually mounted in a protective fairing block as shown, and is secured to the boat by a backing pad and nut.

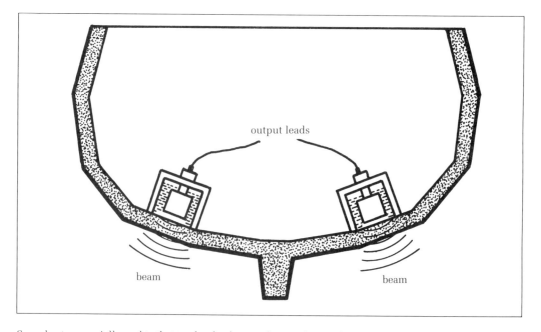

Some boats, especially yachts that tend to heel over when underway, have twin-beam transducers. This means that one echo will always be scanning downwards through the water even with the craft heeled.

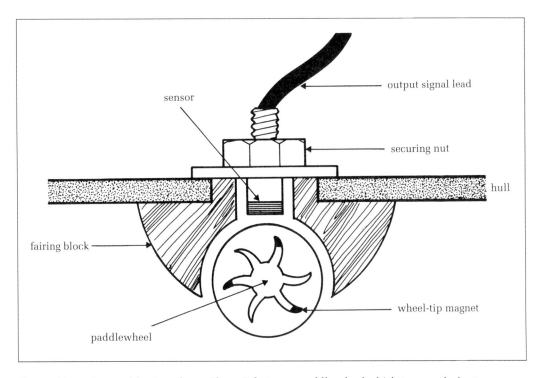

output signal lead

sensor

securing nut

hull

fairing block

wheel-tip magnet

paddlewheel

The workings of a speed-log transducer. The unit features a paddle wheel which turns as the boat moves through the water. The tips of each paddle incorporate a magnet which activate a sensor each time they pass. The resulting signal is passed on to the computer which calculates the boat's speed.

battery to minimize interference from other equipment. To facilitate this the lead is usually supplied already fitted with an in-line fuseholder to protect the equipment. However, this is a far from satisfactory connection method and would be completely impractical on a large boat with a full set of electronics. The best alternative is to run heavy-gauge positive and negative cables from the battery up to an electrical board which has been positioned for easy and convenient access.

Isolating Switches

A heavy-duty battery isolating switch and a fuse or circuit-breaker panel should be fitted to the electrical board for connecting the positive cables. A negative bus bar should also be fitted and need consist of nothing more complicated than a brass bolt mounted on the board. Alternatively, a more sophisticated aluminium or brass strip with connecting screws along its length can be used to allow the connection of eyelet terminals from the negative lead. The latter arrangement allows each piece of equipment to be connected both positive and negative in a convenient position with no voltage drop and each with a separate fuse. The in-line fuse, if fitted, can be left in the circuit as long as it is placed conveniently for checking. If interference between equip-

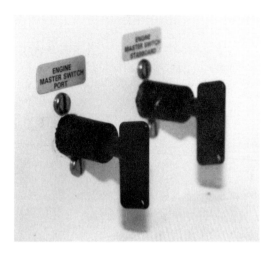

A battery isolation switch is essential to allow the electrical supply to be terminated when the boat is left unattended. It should be mounted in an accessible position where it can be reached easily in case of emergency.

ment is then found, it is unlikely to be cured by connecting directly to the battery so the source must be found elsewhere.

Earthing of electronic equipment will often solve all problems of interference and a third (earthing) cable is often fitted for this purpose. This will usually be coloured green and yellow in the same way as domestic wiring. This may, however, cause a lot of confusion to the uninitiated when faced with three cables – red positive, black negative, and green and yellow earth, and only two battery terminals! The set-up is actually quite simple: the red and black cables are the positive and negative to the battery (or electrical board), while the earth needs to be grounded in the sea. This earth can sometimes be achieved satisfactorily by connecting to the engine as this is in contact with sea water for cooling purposes. The proper and most satis-

factory method, however, is to bolt a sintered (porous for maximum earthing effect) bronze plate, specially designed for the job, through to the bottom of the hull. Earth cables of all the equipment supplied with the third cable are connected to this via one of the through-bolts in the bilge. Steel boats do not require the plate as they are already grounded and the cables can be connected to any convenient piece of steelwork to achieve the same effect. This will often solve all interference problems.

The most severe interference problems generally occur when the engine is running. Interference can be caused by the charging circuit and by the ignition circuits of petrol engines, including outboards. A good tip with outboard motors is to line the inside of the engine cover with aluminium kitchen foil; this will often help matters and yet involve minimal outlay. If a piece of equipment operates perfectly when the boat is at anchor, but suffers from interference as soon as the engine is started, the cause is almost certainly to do with the charging or ignition circuit. This can often be overcome by fitting suppressors to the alternator and ignition coil – use suppressors from car accessory shops designed for cutting interference on car radios.

Power-unit-generated interference can also come from the revolving propeller shaft. Such interference is indicated if the unit operates satisfactorily with the engine running in neutral but the interference increases with the boat's speed once under way. This is another case where earthing can do the trick. Several companies offer simple carbon-brush arrangements which are designed to run on the propeller shaft with a cable connection to the engine or earth plate. However, the same result can be achieved by bridging across the flexible shaft coupling with cable and eyelet connectors to the coupling holding bolts on shaft and gearbox.

Antenna Cables

Returning to the installation guide-lines supplied by equipment manufacturers, another favourite instruction is to run the antenna lead separately from other antenna leads. Again, this is just about impossible to achieve where several items of equipment are involved. Problems with the antenna leads are not usually great and the screening incorporated in these leads is usually sufficient to prevent mutual interference. If interference is found to occur between two particular items and the source is traced to the

antenna leads it is usually possible to solve the problem by running them on opposite sides of the wheelhouse. Even a separation gap of just a few inches will often cure the problem.

The antennae themselves should also be mounted with due regard to each other. Radar scanners emit powerful signals, so it is desirable to mount other antennae out of a direct line – either above or below. Navigator antennae appreciate an uncluttered field around them for clear signal reception, and to simplify the mounting of multiple aerials there are now available multi-function antennae which can handle several signal sources such as Navtex, Decca, VHF and broad-cast. They are designed for neatness and obviously assist in the prevention of interference.

SUMMARY

- Electronic charting does not replace the paper chart; it simply augments it. The most ardent electronic *aficionado* would be an idiot to leave port without an up-to-date paper chart of his cruising area.

- Electronics enhance cruising enjoyment by taking the drudgery out of navigation and almost always offer far greater accuracy than even the most astute navigator.

- The Decca navigation system has been in use for many years on commercial and large fishing vessels, but it is only relatively recently that the development of the silicon chip has made small units suitable for private pleasure craft and angling boats both possible and affordable.

- Satellite navigation has now been in existence for over twenty-five years, but it was the advent of the ubiquitous microchip and microprocessor technology that enabled receivers to be smaller, cheaper and more reliable, and – important to the small pleasure boat owner – to consume less power.

- The need for a boat's crew to be updated regularly with new navigation and weather information is now considered an essential part of modern motorboating.

- Interference to the VHF radio or satellite navigator can often be overcome by fitting suppressors to the alternator and ignition coil of the boat's engine – use suppressors from car-accessory shops designed for cutting interference on car radios.

2
RADAR SYSTEMS

Radar was first invented just before World War II as a means of naval defence, but over the last fifty years it has been refined to such an extent that it can now be considered almost an essential item for the pleasure-boat owner. Electronic miniaturization has increased the range of small-boat radar equipment and, as a result, has not only reduced the cost of a system but has meant that many more boat owners can now afford to fit what was originally an expensive extra. Radar has many uses aboard a boat, the principal one being collision avoidance. However, used intelligently it can also become a sensitive and useful navigation tool ideal for, say, piloting your way into and out of harbour in fog or picking up a mooring buoy in poor visibility. The other main use is position-fixing which, as

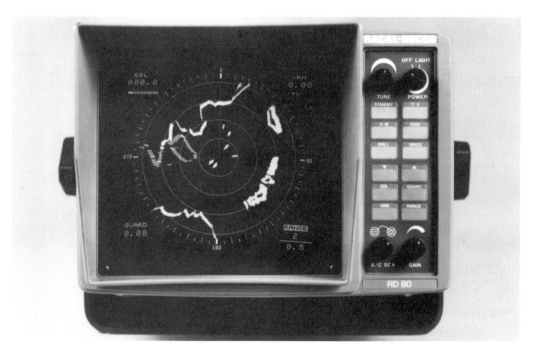

One of the new generation of small-boat radar sets, this model is compact and can easily be fitted to boats of all types.

those who regularly use a radar set will confirm, occurs much more often than the need to avoid collision!

Look on the radar display screen as a 'real time' painting of what is going on around your boat. You will be able to see your boat (the dot at the centre of the circular screen) in relation to other craft, buoys and navigation marks, and coastal landmasses, islands and so on. Radar is also extremely useful when cruising at night, something many boat owners like to do when more experienced, and will help in identifying strange harbours, channel markers and peninsulas. It can be used when approaching an anchorage, ensuring that you steer the correct bearing and, by measuring off the distance from your known position to at least two known points on shore it will enable you to steer the boat by following the range markers on the radar screen until they correspond with the ones plotted.

Integration With Other Systems

Many modern radar sets can now be integrated fully with other navigation and position-finding equipment like Decca, satnav and GPS, and can even be interfaced with an autopilot and chart plotter. This has been made possible as the different manufacturers have agreed on a standard for integration. Connections are made via multicore plugs and sockets, linking the various navigation instruments together. A special computer program allows each item to 'handshake' with its neighbour, thus completing the integration. Latitude and longitude can also be shown on the radar screen, along with Decca waypoints and information

from the satellite navigator, as well as the usual visual picture from the scanner.

Basic Operation

The working principal of radar is relatively simple to explain. Basically, four separate sections are employed: transmitter, antenna (these are combined together in the scanner or radome), receiver and visual display. The radome is instantly recognizable as the swivelling arm on the outside of the boat, but on most modern small-boat sets this is now encased in a GRP dome and no movement can be seen from the outside. This enclosed system looks much neater and is far easier to install.

The transmitter sends out short pulses or spikes of radio energy at a very high frequency, and as it rotates these pulses are emitted in a 360-degree circle after which they are reflected back from any solid object that they strike. The reflected pulses are then processed electronically by the radar's computer before being converted digitally and displayed on the screen. Although the pulse is transmitted in a horizontal mode, the information when converted and displayed will show a bird's-eye view of the situation, as if you were looking from above. The central point on the display screen can be determined as the position of the boat, and it is from this point that all navigation calculations are made.

Pulse Transmission

The transmitted pulses are very short in duration because the receiver cannot start to receive them until the transmitter has stopped sending them out. The actual transmit time is measured in micro-seconds, a radar pulse travelling at the rate of one mile every 6.2 microseconds. Typically, the pulse will be 0.1 micro-seconds on shorter distance ranges during which time it will have travelled 30 metres. On the longer ranges more power is required to push the pulses out over greater distances. For the average pleasure boat with an overall length of around 40–50 feet, a radar with a range of about 24–32km (15–20 miles) should be con-sidered. The power requirements for this size of set are in the region of 40 watts and will operate from either a 12- or 24-volt DC supply.

Always do a little research before buying: ask your dealer questions and try to select a manufacturer with a good name. Many owners save money and get enjoyment from fitting the radar them-selves, and as long as this is performed in conjunction with the radar's supplier it should cause no real problem.

The radar consists of a radome or scanner – either mounted in its own GRP encasement inside which it rotates, or free-mounted in the form of a swinging arm – and the display screen and controls. The most common type is the enclosed radome which is usually mounted as high up as possible on the boat to aid optimum performance. This performance can be attenuated con-siderably by the curvature of the Earth as can be seen in the diagram on page 31. The range of the radar depends upon the correct siting of this radome; and, if it is mounted low down on the boat just because it looks good in this position, serious deficiencies in the range may result.

Fitting a Radar

Scanner Unit

The mounting of the scanner is probably the most important part of the entire installation. Where you mount it on the boat will, to a large extent, determine the performance and range capabilities of the set. The general rule is to mount the radome as high on the boat as possible. Remember that the pulses transmitted and received by the scanner work on a line of sight, and a scanner mounted in front of a wheelhouse roof for example, or on a pulpit rail, will reduce the range and might even blank off part of the scanned circle. Safety is another reason for mount-ing the radome as high as possible. Radar

This radar scanner has been mounted in a good position high on the staysail mast aboard a motor-sailer. A clear view over 360 degrees is desirable for accuracy and to avoid interference.

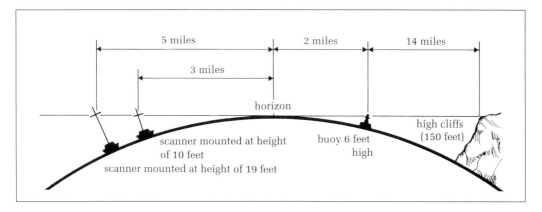

This diagram shows the difference in radar scanning range with the scanner mounted at a height of 10 feet and 19 feet on the boat. Note how the curvature of the Earth's surface can dramatically affect the radar's range.

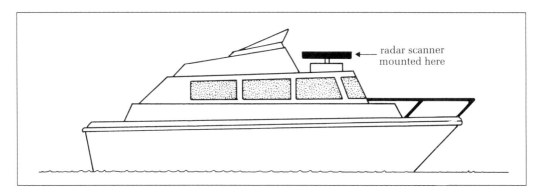

Mounting the radar scanner low down as on the foredeck of this motor boat is bad practice. A short mast should be used to raise it above the height of the boat's superstructure for a clear, 360-degree view.

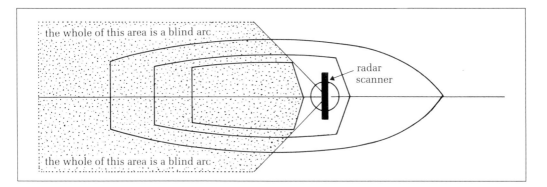

One of the results of mounting a scanner too low is that a considerable portion of the scanning zone will be blanked off, causing inaccuracies and poor performance.

uses microwaves similar to those generated by a microwave oven in the home. Serious eye damage can result if a member of the boat's crew looks directly into the beam path of the scanner when the radar is operating.

Most manufacturers will be able to supply a selection of scanner-mounting brackets suitable for all types of boat, from masthead mounts on yachts to short, stubby masts for cruisers with little above water height. It might be a good plan to take along a drawing or photograph, or a note of the height of your boat above the water-line when shopping around for a radar set.

Scanner Cable

The radar scanner is connected to the display unit by a thick multicore cable. Sets are normally provided with a length of this cable sufficient to allow the scanner to be mounted up a mast and with the display in the cabin or wheelhouse below. Extensions can be bought and some chandlers or marine electricians will supply cable off the roll. The cable should be routed carefully through the boat avoiding the usual sharp corners, and only using waterproof plugs and sockets in places where the cable must pass from the outside of the boat to the inside.

One end of the cable should be stripped back of insulation and connected into the GRP casing of the scanner unit. The set will be supplied with a handbook from which you can work out colour codes and terminal connections. Replace the

The cable from the radar scanner will have to pass through to the inside of the boat. The only safe way of doing this is to use marine-grade waterproof deck plugs and sockets.

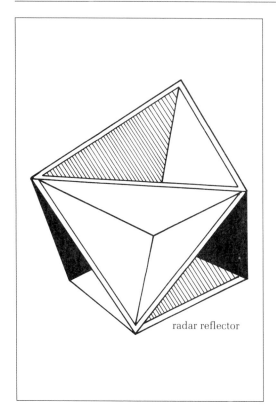

radar reflector

All craft should have the radar reflector fitted at the highest point. This popular type is made from aluminium constructed in a special shape and will enhance the vessels 'reflectivity', enabling it to be picked up more easily on other boat's radar sets.

scanner dome and mount it in your chosen spot. Care should be taken here to ensure that the scanner is pointing in a fore and aft direction. An arrow some-where on the unit will indicate this. If slightly off skew, an incorrect reading will result on the display, throwing out cal-culations and the overall accuracy of the unit.

Never run the cable in such a way that it will get snagged by boots or deck gear, or across areas which could cause chafing or cuts. Also, do not allow the cable to kink sharply as this might damage some of the internal small-gauge wires.

The terminal end of the cable will be supplied with a plug which fits into the rear of the radar display. Remember to route this well away from sources of possible interference such as the com-pass, echo-sounder and ignition circuits.

Siting the Display

Where the radar display is sited will de-pend upon personal preference and the size of your boat. Some navigators prefer to mount the display near the helm where they can keep an eye on what is going on – especially important in fog, bad weather or at night. Others prefer to have the unit near the chart table where they can take off the information shown and apply it directly to their electronic or paper charts. Personally, I would opt for installing the unit near the helm as the screen so that the controls are always within sight of the helmsman. Try to rig the display so that it is out of direct sun rays as these can blank out the picture. Shades can be purchased, which clip over the front of the screen rather like special filters available on computer terminals, or you could try making your own from sheets of black flexible plastic and some glue.

Once the bracket and display have been fixed to the boat, the power and scanner cables should be connected. The scanner cable will simply need to be plugged into the multiplug, but power cables need to be run back to the fuse board or distri-bution centre and wired to their own fused circuit. Remember to use the correct gauge of cable (once again, see the manu-facturer's instructions) and make the cable run as short as possible, avoiding other navigation cables like the satellite system where interference might result.

Setting Up

Once the radar is switched on and working, follow the manufacturer's handbook to fine-tune the set to match it to the boat. This will ensure that the radar works at its maximum efficiency. Also remember before starting a DIY installation of a radar to check with your supplier about any invalidity of the guarantee if you fit it yourself. Some manufacturers might insist on an independent check of the installation before you switch it on to ensure that it has been carried out correctly.

SUMMARY

- The dangers of being at sea in a thick fog or mist, even if you know where you are on your chart when the fog comes down, is a very frightening and sobering experience but one that can be alleviated by the installation of a radar set.

- The radar is a very useful navigation tool which enables the user to identify coastlines, harbour entrances, navigation buoys, moored boats and other obstructions.

- When purchasing a radar remember to choose a reputable manufacturer and be prepared to shop around to get the best possible price. Even more money can be saved if you fit the radar yourself – a task that, with consultation with the manufacturer and supplier, should be quite within your capabilities.

- The radome scanner should have a clear 360-degree view and should not be mounted in a position where part of the boat – for instance, the cabin top – will obscure that view.

- The screen and controls of the radar need to be visible from the helm and should be shaded if possible to prevent direct sunlight from blanking out the picture.

3

COMMUNICATIONS SYSTEMS

The VHF radio is an essential part of your boat's equipment. It is useful for communicating with other craft and land-based installations, for assisting with entry into harbours and ports, and for obtaining the position of other craft and the latest weather information. However, people new to boating may not fully be aware of the implications and limitations of the VHF radio, and the fact that rules and regulations have been laid down for both operators and radio-telephone equipment.

A range of VHF communications equipment from ICOM. Various sizes and specification sets can be seen along with three hand-held units.

It is the availability of up-to-the-minute weather and navigational information, along with added security of safety at sea as a bonus to normal communication use, have encouraged the sales of VHF marine-band radio-telephones to continue to rise over the last fifteen years. The increased sales and the advent of micro-electronics have resulted in the availability of a wide range of equipment (including some very compact sets which incorporate the latest in technological developments). Currently, there are many models available which have been designed to meet the laid-down specifications and which, when trans-mitting on 25 watts, consume 5 amps on long-range work and 1 watt for short-range communication. Many reliable sets are available at a reasonably low price.

Complete System

The VHF marine radio-telephone equip-ment available from your chandler provides a complete communication sys-tem, although it does differ from most other forms of radio communication in that it is usually rather restricted in range. This can be an advantage as the same frequency can be shared by many other different stations as long as they are not too close to each other. VHF radio-telephones have what is known as a captive effect, which means that if two stations are transmitting simultaneously, while a third station is located within range, one of the transmissions will dominate and may completely wipe the other out. It is therefore essential that proper discipline in transmitting is main-tained and operating procedures are followed; this in turn encourages the amateur to be as professional as possible.

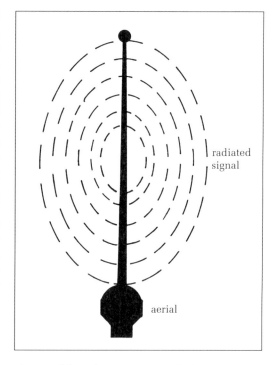

radiated signal

aerial

The signal from the VHF set is pushed out into the ether as radiation from the aerial, and the incoming signal is received in much the same way. If the aerial is not supplied with the set, buy the very best you can afford as it represents the final link in the chain. A poor aerial means bad transmission and reception.

Output

The maximum power output for a VHF on a boat is limited to a maximum of 25 watts, while a low power output of only 1 watt is encouraged for short-range trans-mission. Any old aerial may give some sort of reception, but it may prove useless for transmission. In reality the height of the aerial is most important in order to achieve a satisfactory range. In many cases the fitting of a VHF is a relatively simple task for the handyman and requires no specialized tools. Incidentally, a typical 12-volt installation transmitting on 25 watts consumes about 5 amps of current. Most sets incorporate what is known as simplex operation, which is an operating method for alternative transmission. This allows the set either to transmit or to receive, but not simultaneously like an ordinary land-based telephone. The change-over is, however, accomplished automatically by means of a press-to-speak switch incorporated on the microphone.

Frequencies

The frequencies allocated by inter-national agreement for use by vessels fitted with VHF is between 156.00MHz and 174.00MHz. This band, called the maritime band, is subdivided into a number of channels. These may at first seem to be numbered in an illogical manner, for although there are at least fifty-five channels available for use, those numbered between 29 and 59 are used for other services. Channel 6 is the primary intership frequency, with Channel 16 being the VHF distress and call channel. Contact is usually initially made on Channel 16 before transfer to another channel to conduct the communication. Many sets have a channel-watch facility incorporated which means the operator can automatically monitor two channels

---

THE PHONETIC ALPHABET

Occasionally, in poor transmit/receive conditions, you may have to spell certain words; this is a problem that can also arise when cruising in foreign waters. You may, for instance, need to spell out the name of your boat, which is where the phonetic alphabet comes in. It is easy to memorize but it may be an idea to keep a copy next to your VHF radio installation. Have the name of your craft and your call sign nearby, also spelt in phonetics.

Letter	Word	Spoken as	Letter	Word	Spoken as
A	Alfa	*AL* FAH	N	November	NO *VEM* BER
B	Bravo	*BRAH* VOH	O	Oscar	*OSS* CAH
C	Charlie	*CHAR* LEE	P	Papa	PAH *PAH*
D	Delta	*DELL* TAH	Q	Quebec	KEH *BECK*
E	Echo	*ECK* OH	R	Romeo	*ROW* ME OH
F	Foxtrot	*FOKS* TROT	S	Sierra	SEE *AIR* RAH
G	Golf	GOLF	T	Tango	*TANG* GO
H	Hotel	*HOH* TELL	U	Uniform	*YOU* NEE FORM
I	India	*IN* DEE AH	V	Victor	*VIK* TAH
J	Juliet	*JEW* LEE *ETT*	W	Whiskey	*WISS* KEY
K	Kilo	*KEE* LOH	X	X-ray	*ECKS* RAY
L	Lima	*LEE* MAH	Y	Yankee	*YANG* KEY
M	Mike	MIKE	Z	Zulu	*ZOO* LOO

The syllables in italics should be emphasized during communication

---

The phonetic alphabet is an excellent way of making yourself heard and understood over the VHF radio. I always keep a copy of it stuck up at the helm of my boat near the VHF.

at the same time without having to switch from channel to channel manually. This is useful when monitoring both a port frequency and Channel 16.

Licences

All radio equipment for marine use must have a licence, and fines and confiscation can result from the use of unlicensed equipment. Remember that officials monitor the air waves regularly and if you use radio equipment on your vessel and do not have a valid licence you are liable to prosecution. A Ship Licence authorizes the use of VHF marine radio-telephone receiving and transmitting equipment on a boat. These licences are issued only under certain conditions, one of which is that the radio must be operated only by someone who holds an appropriate certificate of competence. Most other conditions relate to the frequencies which may be used and the maximum power output of equipment, along with the economical use of such equipment and the avoidance of interference.

The operator's certificate of competence known as the Restricted Certificate of Competence in Radio-telephony (VHF only) is awarded only after an examination in radio-telephony – required under the provision of Section 7(1) of the Wireless Telegraphic Act 1949 and the Radio Regulations annexed to International Convention 1973 – and after the holder has made a declaration of secrecy in the operation of radio apparatus. In addition, a passport-sized photograph is needed along with the payment of a small examination fee. In reality, the examination for the certificate is quite simple. It consists of a written and verbal test of the candidate's knowledge of the appropriate procedures and regulations involved in the use of the equipment. Such examinations are carried out regularly around the UK as well as at the major boat shows, and a list of examination centres can be obtained from the Royal Yachting Association. The RYA also produce a very useful booklet (*G26*) which sets out the full syllabus, along with details of the form and arrangements of examination.

VHF Facilities

The popular makes of VHF radio will feature all fifty-five international channels, LED function lights, dual-watch facility and Channel 16 override, while many include extra features such as the automatic blocking of incorrect channel selection and the provision for up to 130 private channels. The majority of the compact radio sets measure only about 8cm (3in) high, with a width in the region of 22cm (8½in) and around 25cm (10in) in depth.

Installation

Designed for installation in a vessel with a 12-volt DC supply, the fitting of a VHF radio-telephone is a relatively simple operation. The supplied mounting bracket (which is secured with a few screws) can go under or over the set so that it can easily be installed in a number of different locations – for example, on a shelf, on a bulkhead, or suspended from overhead. Because all the controls along with the microphone plug and speaker are, in most cases, located on the front panel, this conveniently allows the set to be flush-mounted in a dash panel or other type of overhead cockpit console.

Location

Despite the fact that these radios are built for marine use, to ensure that they give many years of trouble-free service they should be located safely away from the effects of the elements. Obviously, water can cause severe electrical and mechanical damage to your set, so besides ensuring its protection make sure that the set's electrical supply will not be affected. Excessive heat is also a potential problem for all electronic equipment, so the radio should not be installed in direct sunlight. Remember that electronics do generate heat, so allow a free flow of air to circulate around the radio set, especially at the rear end where the output power transistors or integrated circuit is located. The set, whether it is switched on or not, could affect the operation of the boat's compass, and so they should not be positioned within 45 cm (1¾in) of each other.

Connections

At the rear of the radio are the various plugs, including the connection for the power supply as well as those for the aerial and external speaker. Supplied with your set is the power cable with an in-line fuseholder and fuse, along with a plug for the rear of the radio. The power supply is all important and whenever possible the power lead for your radio should be connected straight to the battery via an isolating switch. The positive red wire connects to the + terminal and the black negative wire to the – terminal. In all probability you will need to extend the leads, and if this is the case use wire no smaller than 10 gauge –

even then keep the extension as short as possible to avoid unnecessary interference and voltage drop.

Try to avoid running cables alongside other power wires, especially those carrying substantial amounts of energy such as cables associated with the radar and its scanner. Any connections must be made with an approved plug and socket. Best of all is a waterproof unit with a captive screw cap to provide weatherproofing when the socket is not in use. If the power cable has to go through a bulkhead, use a cable gland or rubber grommet to prevent chafing and possible short circuiting.

Interference Suppression

VHF radios operate in the 150MHz band and are relatively free of interference from other electrical devices such as ignition systems, alternators and windscreen-wiper motors. On the other hand, engine

For a strong, interference-free signal on VHF or Decca, make sure that a proper coaxial aerial connector is used – especially if you need to extend the cable over a long run.

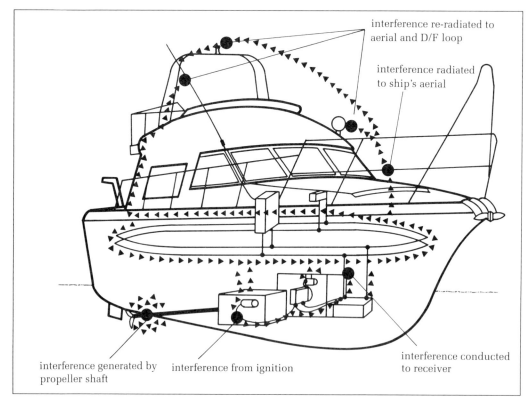

interference re-radiated to aerial and D/F loop

interference radiated to ship's aerial

interference conducted to receiver

interference generated by propeller shaft

interference from ignition

The various routes that interference can take on an average motor-boat. (Courtesy of Lucas Marine.)

rev counters can be a source of trouble, so do avoid putting these and their power supply close to the radio. Some rev counters may have to be shielded or have filters installed. Some of the older voltage regulators are also a source of trouble and can cause a 'zizzing' noise to emit from your set. However, this problem can usually be rectified by fitting suppression capacitors which can be bought from your local motoring-accessory shop.

Aerials

A radio signal is an alternating wave of electromagnetic energy, generated to a particular alternating frequency by the radio's circuitry, and expelled into the atmosphere via the radio aerial. Because of its technicality, it is difficult to explain easily the working of the all-important aerial and its capabilities. Suffice it to say that the range of VHF transmission and reception is governed by a number of factors including humidity, height and atmospheric conditions. The higher the antenna, the more the gain and therefore the greater the range. However, in all cases the antenna lead should be kept as short as possible. If the lead does require extending, use only proper coaxial cable with the correct sort of coupling. Taped

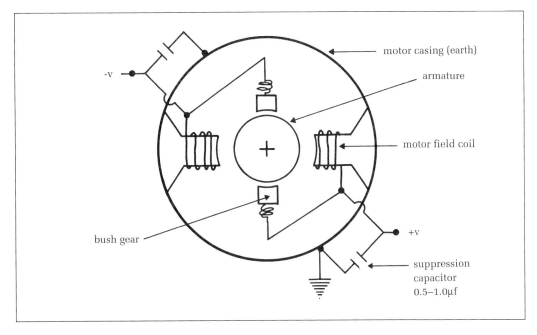

One very good method of stopping the interference from an electric motor is to fit a low-value suppression capacitor in the motor armature circuit as shown here. Capacitors can be bought from most motor-accessory shops or electronic hobbyist stores.

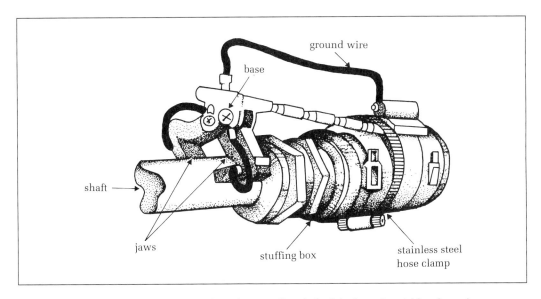

A device which suppresses interference from the propeller shaft of the boat. Special brushes rub on the shaft as it turns and are grounded, taking the RFI to earth.

41

joints just will not do!

There are many aerials available, ranging from a short helical type with the aerial wound and encased in rubber, and often found on hand-held sets, to others several metres in length. A 1m (3ft) long stainless steel whip type is very strong, yet light and flexible with low windage; it is ideal for fast-moving craft such as sports boats where the continuous motion could result in the structural failure of a more rigidly constructed aerial. Light-weight glass-fibre covered aerials are gen-erally accepted as the best for most motor boats and range from models with an overall length of 1m (3ft) with a base that fits firmly on a short side bracket, to larger models that taper. The latter have a screw-fastening swivel base that allows for the vertical positioning of the aerial despite the angle of the base to which it is fitted. Most models available have a frequency range of 156–162MHz and are all sup-plied with cable up to 18m (20yd) in length. In most cases this length of cable will be long enough to plug straight into the radio without the need for jointing.

As most cables will need to pass through a deck or bulkhead to the outside of the boat, a waterproof deck gland to effect a seal should be used. If a con-nection is needed, consider using a water-proof in-line connector with rubber boots surrounding it, or alternatively a water-proof deck connector kit that both facilitates passage through the deck and allows for the easy removal of the aerial. The lengthy glass-fibre aerial will snap into two if it hits a bridge or other over-head obstruction, and to avoid this it would be best to use a swivel-mounted base. With the base of the aerial screwing into the bracket, the use of a cam lock allows the aerial to be swivelled through 180 degrees so that it can be dropped quickly out of harm's way.

SUMMARY

- The VHF is a useful link to the land-based telephone network and can be used to glean a whole variety of information on weather forecasts and navigational warnings, to gain access to the coastguard or to book your overnight berth at a distant marina.

- The most important channel with priority over all others is the Call and Distress channel – Channel 16 – and an understanding of its use and operation is essential.

- Although most VHFs are designed specifically for use in a wet environment, care should be exercised when siting the unit on board the boat.

- The VHF aerial is a most important part of your installation. It is the final link in the chain of events that forms your transmission/reception line and should be the best that you can afford.

- Interference can have a very marked effect on the performance of your VHF radio as well as some of the more sensitive items of electronic navigation equipment, such as the digital fluxgate compass, radar and Decca navigation system.

4
FRESHWATER
SYSTEMS

If you own a simple day boat or open boat, your freshwater system may not comprise anything more complicated than a simple plastic container with which to dispense your water, this probably being needed only for making a cup of tea and doing the washing up. For the larger, more elaborate motor cruisers with several cabins, more than one toilet compartment, a shower, hand basin and a full galley, however, the system installed is much more complex. The system you choose will obviously depend upon the number and nature of the functions supplied aboard.

Many boaters who have fallen foul of mysterious illnesses often blamed on food poisoning or sea-sickness may really have been suffering from contaminated or diseased water without realizing the cause, so the provision of a freshwater supply for all crew members should be given maximum priority. All mains drinking water is specially filtered and treated to keep it fresh, so the tap you use to fill your boat's freshwater tank should always be a bonafide drinking-water tap.

Once the water is in your tank its quality starts to diminish, although it can remain in a drinkable state for several weeks or months. The idea is to keep fresh water flowing through the system regularly, which does not necessarily

One of the simplest ways of providing fresh water on a small cruiser. This moulded GRP sink is fitted with a hand pump supplied from a 5-gallon drum in the cupboard below.

mean that you must always fill the tanks to capacity but rather ensure that you have enough water on board to be sufficient for the needs of the voyage. In this way there is less chance of a build-up in contaminating bacteria in the water as would happen if the tanks were left topped up for long periods without use.

There are several kinds of purification which can be applied directly and indirectly to the water in the form of chemical tablets and filters, and these are discussed later in this chapter (*see* page 48). Any water, however fresh when piped in, will eventually become contaminated if it is stored in the closed system (water-tank piping and pump) of a boat. This will show up as bad-smelling and tasting water and the complete system will eventually need flushing out with a cleansing chemical.

Let us now look at some of the systems available for the supply of hot and cold water in your craft.

The System

In its simplest form, a boat's water system consists of a storage tank with filler pipe and sealed cap situated somewhere on the outside of the boat (usually on deck or on

a gunwhale), an outlet pipe from the tank coupled to the inlet of a pumping device, and a pipe from the pump to the tap. It will be a cold-water system only and may supply one hand-pumped tap on a small sink in the galley. The outlet from this sink is usually another pipe attached to a hull-skin fitting, the waste water being expelled overboard.

The beauty of this system is that it can be adapted to your requirements with very little effort. Secondary pipes can be connected to the main pump outlet to supply a hand basin, the cold leg of a shower and to feed a toilet-flush system. Systems can be activated electronically by turning on a tap, and you can also have a separate sea-water supply for general use such as washing up or sluicing down the decks.

Pumps

Pumps are varied and diverse. There are pumps available to suit just about every

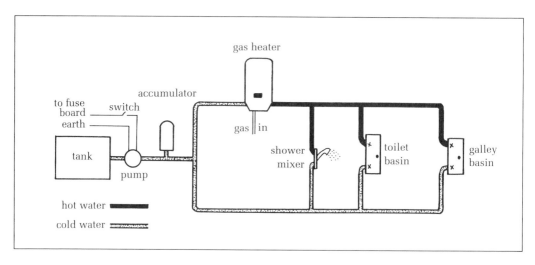

The circuit of a simple boat hot and cold domestic water system, incorporating pump, tank, gas heater and tap/shower outlets.

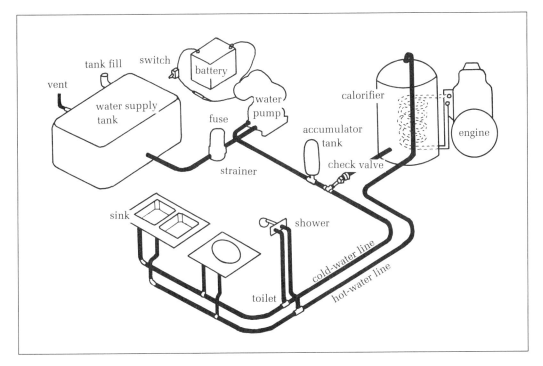

Schematic diagram of a complete boat domestic water system. This shows a calorifier which takes waste heat from the boat's engine and stores it in an immersion tank ready for later use. A good calorifier will produce plenty of hot water even after the engine has run for only twenty minutes.

water system that has ever been conceived, as well as for bilge emptying and flood-pumping work.

The pumps come in all shapes and sizes. Some are heavy-duty versions which can supply a good head of water over a considerable distance – a must when metres of interconnecting pipe and several taps are used. The problem with a weaker flow pump is that at the furthest point from the tank the pressure is reduced so much that it can result in a mere trickle at the tap.

Bearing in mind that the water supply on board is a limited one, it is probably best to choose a mechanically operated pump for your main supply. These can be foot operated and fitted to the floor in a convenient place. They are electrically powered, but as soon as the foot pressure is removed from the switch the pump stops, thus eliminating the problems of running the tank dry through overzealous use of running water (a problem when cleaning your teeth or working in the galley). Hand-operated switch pumps that work on a similar principle are also available.

Taps

Electric taps are usually 12 volt and have a microswitch in their tops to activate the water pump when the tap is turned on.

The fresh water is supplied to the various taps, shower heads and toilets around the boat by a single main water pump. This one is being drained of water for servicing.

Some work by having a pressure switch on the pump which is activated automatically by the reduction of pressure in the system when a tap is turned on. Others include special thin tubular switches operated by 12 volts and which can be inserted directly into the water tank or container itself, but these are for small-bore systems and produce a very low pressurized output.

Holding Tank

The water-holding tank is one of the most important features of any boat's water system, second perhaps only to the pump. Once again, there are several types on the market to suit individual needs.

Tanks can be fabricated in stainless steel, mild steel or polypropylene, and can be shaped or moulded to fit any particular space in the hull or under the floor of the boat. They can also be as large or as small as required – an average capacity for a motor cruiser of, say, 30 feet is around 450 litres (100 gallons), but larger boats may have tanks of up to 900 litres (200 gallons) or more. Smaller boats in the range 16–20 feet may have a tank capacity of only 300 litres (70 gallons), while anything smaller will just have a portable container. With some systems, the tanks can be linked together in 45-litre (10-gallon) increments, which allows for a greater degree of flexibility when siting the tanks in the boat.

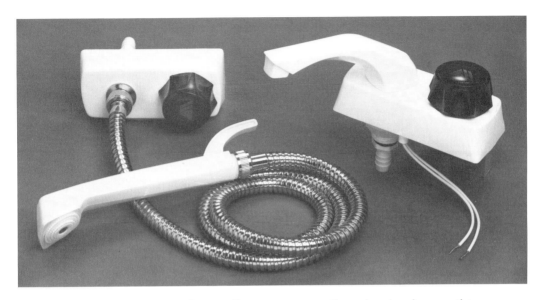

You can buy a range of taps to suit all types of boat water system. Shown here is a shower outlet and a single microswitch-operated faucet.

Whether one tank is better than another is a debatable point, and nothing has really been proved on the subject of algae build-up in different tank types. A tank with an accessible inspection hatch is probably a good idea so that, if necessary, you can get an arm in to clean it out, but this is not essential.

If you are fitting out a boat from scratch and have an ideal area or shape in which to fit your tank, you should have either a stainless-steel or polypropylene tank fabricated and moulded to your exact requirements. This is slightly more expensive than buying a ready-built tank, but it is usually worth while. Remember when siting the tank on a new hull that problems might arise with ballasting – a tank full of water can have a dramatic effect on the trim of the boat.

Taps and Showers

A wide variety of taps and shower heads are available to fit most sinks, both the special boat type and the larger domestic size. Aquaflow in particular have a good range, from very simple bent alloy pipes with a coupling for the water pipe below, to twin hot and cold electrically operated fawcets in chrome or plastic and special multi-angled taps which will fit curved- or straight-sink surface mounts.

Taps can be chosen to match the other equipment and décor in the boat. Most are simple to fit, requiring only a single nut to secure them from below. The supply pipe is then pressed on to the tap flange and secured either with a jubilee clip or one of the special acetal hose clips currently available. The spouts of most taps can be moved back to give more room at the sink or to allow the use of a worktop cover which provides more work space.

Showers range from a combination tap/shower head in the smaller compartment, where the spout of the tap is also employed as the shower rose, to special thermostatically controlled units with mixer taps and adjustable heights. Many domestic-style shower heads such as the popular Mira models can also be used, provided the pipe connections fit the rest of the system.

Pipes

Most of the pipework used to connect the simpler water systems consists of special food-grade plastic hose – usually colour coded, blue indicating cold and red indicating hot. It runs into confined areas of the bilge or behind cladding, and is easy to cut and push on to the outlets of pumps, taps and tanks. Many pipes are designed to resist the formation of algae, but most pick something up after long periods as stagnant water rests in their bores.

In many bigger boats, standard, solid-drawn copper pipe of a domestic size (28mm) is used for both the hot and cold supplies. This is connected by brass compression fittings; corners are overcome by special soldered joints which can be sealed into place by the application of heat from the exterior.

One new system available is called Acorn and consists of lengths of plastic pipe and a series of plastic fittings. The pipes can be cut to size using a small hacksaw and the fittings pushed on and tightened by hand, no other tools being required. The pipework is then supported (as most types are) by several P clips placed at regular intervals along its length. This prevents sagging, vibration and the eventual collapse of joints.

Keeping it Pure

As mentioned earlier, as soon as fresh water is piped into your tank it starts to lose its quality. This is usually first noticed by an unpleasant musty taste in the water, followed by odours similar to those of fish or ripe cucumbers. There are several ways of overcoming this problem, one of the simplest being to chlorinate the water with special tablets. These are manufactured by companies such as VW Products, who make Puriclean and Chempro, and who also make tank-cleaning agents. The tablets are particularly useful on long voyages when a vast quantity of water has to be stored, and in foreign waters where the mains drinking water may not have been treated. Special filtering units can also be bought which purify and filter the water as it is being

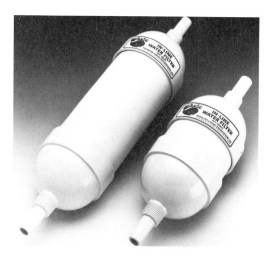

To help keep the purity of the boat's fresh water high, in-line filters can be fitted. They can normally filter water successfully for about a year before the filter cartridge needs to be replaced.

drawn off. These are usually fitted in the main supply line from the pump – simply splice them into the pipework and clip them in place.

Contaminated water that is not fit to drink should not be used for this purpose at all – do not use it for ice cubes as the action of freezing does nothing to cleanse the water. However, water can be boiled to purify it; five or six minutes of boiling is sufficient to kill almost everything. Boiled water tastes dull because much of the oxygen has been removed by the process, but a simple method of replacing the oxygen and the sparkle is to pour the water from one container to another repeatedly and vigorously from a height!

When winter comes or if the boat will not be used for a long period, the main tank should be pumped out and drained, and then washed through with a proprietary flushing agent. The pump should be disconnected at the inlet to prevent any remaining water from freezing and cracking the joints (keeping all taps open will also help prevent this). This is especially important when dealing with water heaters which have small-bore copper-piping feeds.

In the spring, the system can be reconnected and once again flushed through with cleaner before the tank is refilled from a freshwater tap.

SUMMARY

- Many boaters who have fallen foul of mysterious illnesses often blamed on food poisoning or sea-sickness may really have been suffering from contaminated or diseased water without realizing the cause, so the provision of a freshwater supply for all crew members should be given maximum priority.

- In its simplest form, a boat's water system consists of a storage tank with filler pipe and sealed cap situated somewhere on the outside of the boat (usually on deck or on a gunwhale), an outlet pipe from the tank coupled to the inlet of a pumping device, and a pipe from the pump to the tap.

- The water-holding tank is one of the most important features of any boat's water system, second perhaps only to the pump.

- One excellent pipe system called Acorn consists of lengths of plastic pipe and a series of plastic fittings. The pipes can be cut to size using a small hacksaw and the fittings pushed on and tightened by hand, no other tools being required.

- Special filtering units can be bought which purify and filter the water as it is being drawn off. These are usually fitted in the main supply line from the pump – simply splice them into the pipework and clip them in place.

5
PUMP SYSTEMS

I wonder how many boat owners ever give thought to the idea that one day they may be unfortunate enough to have their craft sink beneath them or at its moorings? Even at a slow rate of entry it does not take very long for craft to list over far enough for water to pour into vent holes, air ducts and unprotected sink and shower outlets. The obvious answer is to fit some kind of pump in the bilges which is capable not only of coping with small amounts of rain water, but also with a larger quantity of water which may enter a leaky stern gland or through a holed hull.

It has been said that there is no better type of pump than a frightened man with a bucket, but a frightened man will eventually tire – something that a good-quality, quick-action, high-capacity bilge pump will never do. There are many different types of pump available, ranging from those that sit in the lowest point of the bilge and that can be immersed totally in water, to the manual types that are fitted up top to the side of a bulkhead and operated by hand using a lever. Many of the electric bilge pumps operate from 12 volts DC, and some have an automatic facility which means that they switch themselves on when the water rises to a certain level and off again when the level has gone down to something more acceptable. Pumps vary a great deal in quality and price; they can be either diaphragm, cam or impeller operated and

An average workhorse bilge pump, the Rule 1500 from Aqua-Marine is designed to sit on the bottom of the bilge. It is powered by 12 volts and the outlet can be piped over the side at a convenient point.

some even come with their own kit of spares – essential on a larger river or sea-going craft.

Choosing Your Pump

As I have already said, there is a wide

A 12-volt freshwater pump from Johnson. These are self-contained units and can be fitted in many places, from under the cabin floor to the inside of cupboards.

variety of pumps available: electric, manually operated or even engine driven. Every boat, no matter how large or small, should have at least one manually operated pump with as large a capacity as possible. For craft whose bilges are not divided into sections and all the water drains to one place, the pipework can be plumbed in permanently. For craft with separate bilge compartments pipes can be led from each compartment to a manifold near the pump, where the selection of compartments to be pumped is achieved by turning on the appropriate gate valve. A simpler method which does the same job is to attach a coil of hose to the pump, long enough to reach all the compartments of the bilge and run it out to the area to be pumped when required. This manually operated pump should be mounted within easy reach of the helm position so that the helmsman can operate the pump while steering if the rest of the crew is incapacitated through sea-sickness or injury. Hopefully this dire situation will never arise, but good seamanship means preparing for the worst.

The range of electrically operated pumps for the bilge is even larger than that for the manual ones. Powered by 12 or 24 volts to suit most boats' electrical systems, they are normally mounted 'loose' at the lowest point in the bilge (in many boats this is the engine compartment) and have a single pipe outlet coupled to a skin fitting above water-level. Many electric types now have an automatic mode fitted as standard, which means that the pump can carry on working even if the boat is left un-attended. This alleviates the problem of forgetting to turn on the pump when you leave the boat.

When buying an electric pump make

sure that during installation the height limits for its suction and water heads are not exceeded. All manufacturers' literature will give the correct height and this is also sometimes labelled on the body of the pump itself. You must also make sure that the correct gauge of cable is used when you come to wire it in.

Let us now look in more detail at a selection of the most popular pump types available to the boat owner.

Manual Pumps

Simple Bailers

Probably the simplest implement for removing water from the interior of a boat is the hand bailer. There are several types on the market and all are made of plastic, are cheap and look very much like a dust pan in shape. Such bailers have a very minor role – bailing out dinghies or small day boats – and have little use on a larger cruiser or narrow boat.

On smaller boats a manual bilge pump can be fitted. This cut-away shows a Henderson manual pump fitted through the deck surface. The pump is worked by a tough rubber diaphragm.

Stirrup-Type Pumps

The upright manual stirrup-type pump comes next. The end of it is placed in the offending water, the outlet pipe is fed over the side and a single hand lever is moved up and down to do the pumping. These pumps can be fitted to the gunwale of small boats or used loose, but they too are difficult to use in a confined area such as an engine compartment and should be disregarded for serious use.

Diaphragm Pumps

Large-capacity manual pumps on small boats are usually of the diaphragm type.

These pumps are able to shift very large quantities of water (even more so with the double-action types), and have the added advantage of being able to pump quite large lumps of debris without choking. In the event of a blockage occurring they are easy and quick to clean out and are also simple to service.

The pump is mounted on a bulkhead where the action of swinging a lever pushes a rubber or neoprene diaphragm to and fro, thereby drawing water in through a non-return valve and expelling it through an outlet pipe. Because of the large size of these pumps and their associated levers, they must always be mounted securely to the bulkhead and the pipes must be clipped and routed firmly in place.

Semi-Rotary Pumps

Another type of manual pump is the semi-rotary. These are now somewhat old-fashioned for use as bilge pumps and instead are generally utilized for fuel transference. They are quite heavy, being made of iron and brass, and have a relatively low pumping capacity – for instance, a number 5, 1½-inch-bore pump weighs almost 30kg (70lb) and has a capacity of only 70 litres (15 gal) per minute.

Cylinder Pumps

The final type of manual pump is the bulkhead-mounted cylinder type. Operated by an up-and-down pumping action, they have the advantage of being easy to mount in small spaces. They do not have the capacity of the diaphragm type and are also easily choked with bilge debris, so a good strum box is required (*see* page 56). This pump comes in a variety of sizes, and as the smallest are designed to be portable they can be used in any part of the boat, particularly in cramped awkward areas. The very smallest types are often used for changing engine oil. They have a narrow-bore pipe which can be fitted down the dip-stick hole to save the problem of trying to get a draining tray below the engine.

Electric Pumps

Electrically operated bilge pumps come in several different types but the most popular is probably the submersible. The reasons for this are twofold: first, they are relatively cheap to buy and, second, they have an enormous pumping capacity compared with all other types of pump. When considering buying one of these pumps you should remember that you do tend to get what you pay for – the very cheapest models will not have a very long life, while the better known makes will probably last the lifetime of your boat and will also be very much more reliable. The very smallest models also only have a capacity of about 900 litres (200 gallons) per hour, while the largest are capable of shifting over 9,000 litres (2,050 gallons)! They nearly always incorporate a coarse filter which is moulded in as part of the body and this will deal with the majority of large debris. Smaller pieces of rubbish will find their way through, so the pump should be installed in such a position that it is possible to reach it easily for cleaning. Of course, if you keep your bilges clean you will not need to do this very often.

Another advantage is that they can usually run dry without any harm coming to the impeller – handy if you forget to switch the pump off when the bilges have been emptied.

All submersible-type pumps must be mounted below the water-level in order to work. This means that they must be fitted in the lowest part of the bilge; and remember that as they cannot prime themselves, any water below the level of the pump will not be removed. They work by spinning a vane-type turbine at high speed which forces water into the outlet pipe where it is pushed along by the following water.

Other types of electrically operated

53

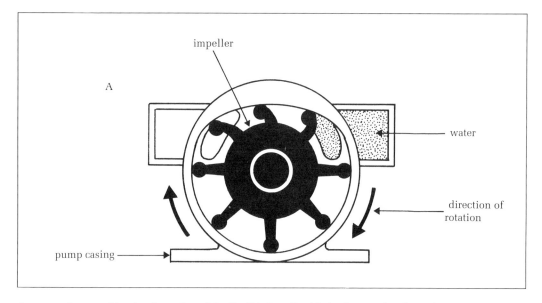

A vacuum is created by the elongation of the flexible impeller blades (pump chamber volume increases) as they retreat from the eccentric cam section of the pump body and liquid is sucked into the pump. (Courtesy of ITT Jabsco.)

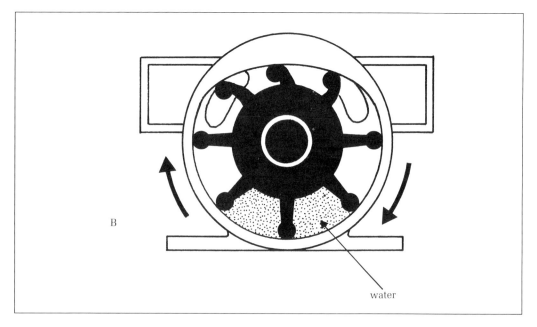

The liquid is carried forward by the rotation of the impeller. As the impeller blades do not bend, even fairly large solids can be passed. (Courtesy of ITT Jabsco.)

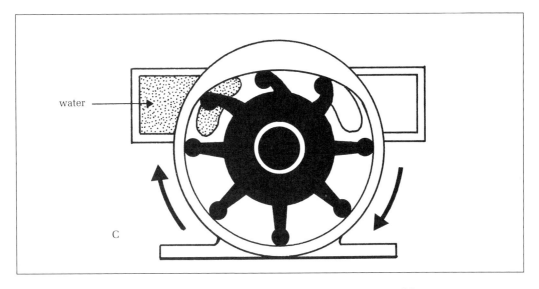

When the flexible impeller blades regain contact with the eccentric cam section of the pump body, the blades are bent and the liquid is discharged from the pump in a uniform flow. (Courtesy of ITT Jabsco.)

pumps are those which use a neoprene or nitrile impeller similar to that in engine-cooling water pumps. These are self-priming which means that they can be mounted out of the bilge in any handy position. They can pass small pieces of debris but have a longer life if the water is filtered before it passes through the system.

Electric Diaphragm Pumps

Electric diaphragm pumps usually utilize a belt drive from a motor leading to a connecting rod which operates the diaphragm, or diaphragms as is the case with larger capacity pumps. These pumps are self-priming and can also run dry without damage, but even the largest models cannot compete with submersibles in terms of pumping capacity.

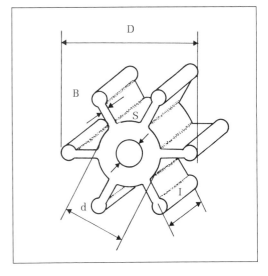

How to identify an impeller which needs to be replaced. (Dimensions are nominal and are given in millimetres.) D=diameter measured over blade tips; l=length measured over impeller faces; d=diameter measured over impeller hub; B=blade thickness; n=number of blades; S=shaft diameter. (Courtesy of ITT Jabsco.)

Most pumps can easily be dismantled for servicing. This photograph shows a manual pump with the rubber diaphragm at the centre of the pump.

To sum up the types of electric pump, submersibles have a huge capacity, are relatively cheap and can run dry without damage, but as they cannot self-prime they must be positioned in the lowest part of the boat. The impeller-type pumps have a good capacity and are self-priming, but they cannot run dry for more than a few moments without the impeller burning out. Electric diaphragm-type pumps can run dry, have a reasonable capacity and are self-priming, but they are usually the most expensive to buy.

Engine-mounted pumps use the same type of impeller as the engine-cooling pump, and are often just another version of the same thing with the added refinement of a manually operated clutch. The largest of these has the capacity to outstrip even the submersible pump, providing sufficient engine revs are available. They cannot be operated dry as they

suffer the same overheating problems as other impeller types, so careful monitoring of water levels is needed to ensure that the pump is disengaged before it runs dry. A more sophisticated version of this pump has an electromagnetic clutch which can be operated remotely. It is even possible to obtain dual-action pumps with twin impellers, one for standard engine cooling and the other (clutch operated) for bilge pumping or deck washing.

Emergency Pump

It should be remembered that all boats with inboard engines carry an emergency bilge pump in the form of the engine-cooling pump. With the addition of two gate valves and a T piece, the inlet can be redirected from the inlet filter to the bilge, thereby pumping bilge water out through the exhaust. Again, careful filtering is essential for successful operation.

Plumbing and Operation

Strum Boxes

To make plumbing simpler, there are T pieces and Y Pieces, and T and Y valves for redirecting suction. Strum box is the nautical term for the coarse filter which is mounted in the bilge to prevent the pump from clogging. Strum boxes are available in many sizes and types for all pump prefiltering duties.

Automatic Switches

For the automatic operation of pumps that are capable of running when dry, there are

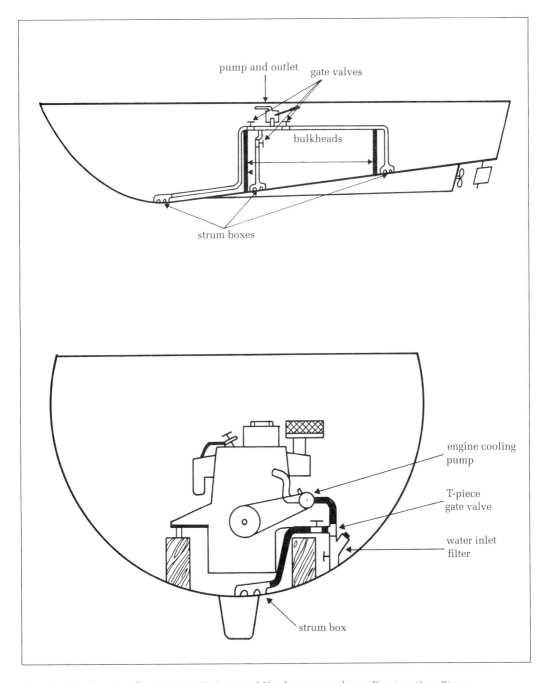

To make plumbing simpler, T pieces, Y pieces and Y valves are used to redirect suction. Strum boxes are available in many sizes and are used as course filters to prevent debris from clogging the workings of the pump. They are fitted as shown.

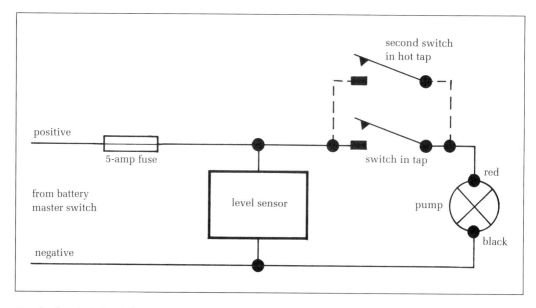

second switch
in hot tap

positive

5-amp fuse

switch in tap

from battery
master switch

level sensor

pump

red

black

negative

Simple electrical circuit for wiring in pressure-operated cold and hot water taps.

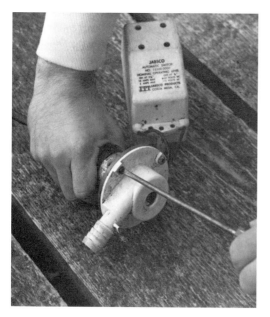

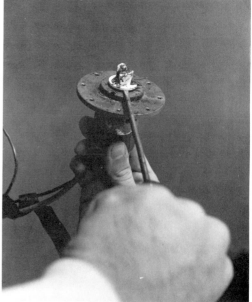

It pays to check your bilge pump regularly. The
one item that is prone to breaking down is the
impeller – the heart of the pump. Removing the
top from the pump will reveal the impeller.

Use a screwdriver to prise off the old impeller
gently. Replacement is a reversal of the
procedure.

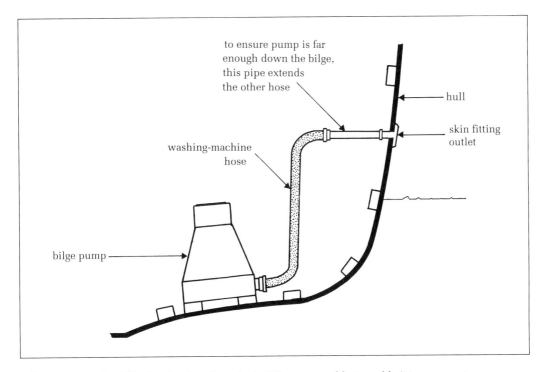

to ensure pump is far
enough down the bilge,
this pipe extends
the other hose

hull

skin fitting
outlet

washing-machine
hose

bilge pump

The bilge pump should be fitted as low down in the bilges as possible to enable it to pump out as much water as it can. A better position can sometimes be achieved by extending the outlet pipe as shown here.

different types of switch available which mount in the bilge and switch the pump on and off as required. Usually, these are float-type switches which consist of a bead of mercury inside a sealed compartment to make and break the contact, but cheaper models use simple switch contacts which generally have a shorter life because of the effects of corrosion and wear. Also available is a solid-state switch which has no moving parts and operates by measuring the sound waves in a central spot. When interrupted by a liquid the pump is switched on, switching off after a timed delay when the water has fallen below the prescribed level.

Pumps for Fresh Water

The freshwater system was dealt with in greater detail in Chapter 4 (*see* page 43), but to recap, freshwater pumps are either of the electrically powered foot-operated variety or the hand-operated switch type which works on a similar principle.

Pump Accessories

There are several accessories and kits available for the improvement, protection and extension of bilge and freshwater pumps, as well as water systems. For example, a pressure-accumulator tank connected to the pressurized side of a freshwater system will assist in producing a much more even flow. Once the tank is fitted the pressure on the water can be adjusted to its most efficient level by a special valve on the tank. Switch panels with a warning light can be fitted to existing bilge pumps along with float and vacuum switches. They work well on self-priming pumps and can be used to prevent the pump from running dry and burning out.

However, the golden rule when it comes to selecting a pump for whatever purpose – bilge or domestic fresh water – is correct siting and selection. There is no substitute for reading through manufacturers' notes and consulting the main dealer or even the manufacturer himself for advice. In the long run this will save time, money and frustration.

SUMMARY

- It has been said that there is no better type of pump than a frightened man with a bucket, but a frightened man will eventually tire – something that a good-quality, quick-action, high-capacity bilge pump will never do.

- Small boats usually use a bulkhead-mounted diaphragm pump where the action of swinging a lever pushes a rubber or neoprene diaphragm to and fro, thereby drawing water in through a non-return valve and expelling it through an outlet pipe.

- Impeller-type pumps have a good capacity and are self-priming, but they cannot run dry for more than a few moments without the impeller burning out. Electric diaphragm-type pumps can run dry, have a reasonable capacity and are self-priming, but they are usually the most expensive to buy.

- For the automatic operation of pumps that are capable of running when dry, there are different types of switch available which mount in the bilge and switch the pump on and off as required. These are ideal for use when the boat is to be left afloat on its own for long periods.

6
GAS SYSTEMS

Most types of boat with cooking or heating equipment, whatever their size, are probably fitted with a bottled gas supply. The type of gas used is called liquid petroleum gas (LPG) and is a highly volatile substance contained under liquid pressure in a metal cylinder. There are two types: butane and propane. Because of its use in the relatively confined space of a boat, the gas system can be dangerous if neglected or treated with disrespect. It is the duty of every boat owner to ensure the safety of the gas installation, and a regular inspection should be carried out at least twice every season and definitely at the end of the year.

The best way to find out about the safe installation of a marine gas system is to contact either the manufacturer or the coastguard service. They will be able to provide leaflets on various systems for different types of boat, many showing detailed diagrams of pipework and bottle storage holders. It is essential that the gas bottle is installed into a fully ventilated compartment preferably outside the main cabins of the boat and somewhere on deck where fresh air is in plentiful supply.

Most boats today have some form of cooking facility on board. This boat is fitted with a full-size domestic cooker which is fuelled by liquid petroleum gas (LPG).

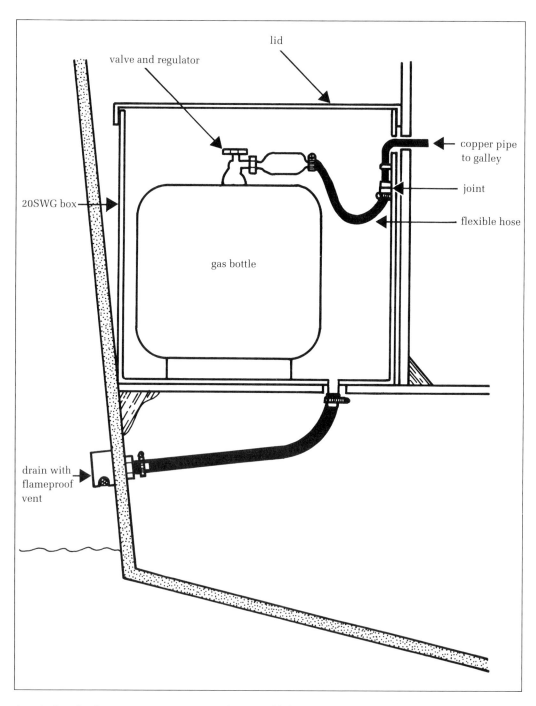

A typical gas bottle compartment – note ventilation and lid.

Certain boats (usually glass-fibre types) have special moulded-in lockers for the bottles on the aft deck. These lockers are self-draining of both water and gas; the latter, being heavier than air, sinks to the lowest part of the boat making it dangerous in the event of a serious leak. Try to install the bottle out of the direct rays of the sun and keep it as sheltered as possible from bad weather. Butane gas is especially prone to freezing in winter and becomes useless at just below freezing point; if you plan to do a lot of winter cruising a better choice of fuel might be propane which has a lower freezing point.

Looking for Leaks

If you suspect a gas leak, the first thing to do is to switch off all the boat's electrical systems including lights – use the main battery isolation switch to do this. Turn off the gas at the main cylinder, open the windows and lift the floorboards to allow fresh air into the bilge area. A useful

method of removing gas from the bilges of a boat is to 'bail' it out using a plastic bucket or bailer. This might look rather strange and cause amused comments, but it is actually an excellent way of moving large volumes of gas and air.

Gas System Accessories

Low Gas Detectors

Among the many detectors and additional gadgets available for the boat's gas system is a 'low gas' warning light. These small fittings can be fitted in any convenient location and simply illuminate when the LPG supply is inadequate, thereby saving the bother of actually checking the gauge adjacent to the bottle. Another type of tester available is a gas-leak unit that is installed in line immediately after the bottle regulator. To satisfy yourself that the LPG system is functioning correctly, simply check that six bubbles a minute appear in a special fluid visible in the tube.

You can now buy a special gas regulator which incorporates a gauge that will tell you how much gas is left in the bottle.

Change-Over Systems

The use of a manual or an automatic change-over system using two bottles avoids the need to search for a spanner and make a physical change-over when the gas supply is exhausted. Such a task can be left until a more timely occasion without any interruption to the supply when one of the change units is installed. The continual supply of gas also avoids the need to relight the pilot lights on the hot-water system and the fridge.

The manual unit comprises a regulator and gauge with two pigtails that terminate in either a threaded male coupling for propane or a threaded ferrule for butane gas. When the LPG supply is nearly exhausted, you simply switch on the back-up cylinder and turn the empty one off in order to maintain supply. With the manual change-over unit you must anticipate when the appropriate switch-over should be made, although this is not a problem with the fitted gauge.

Like the manual unit, the automatic change-over unit is available for both propane and butane. The automatic unit switches over to the back-up bottles as required and you do not even need to leave the tiller. The automatic unit does not have a gauge but instead has a glass-sided indicator that shows either a white or red stripe within the housing. Gaslow Ltd produce an excellent range of change-over systems which are suitable for anyone who has purchased a new boat since they add little to the outlay of a regulator alone.

There are many ways in which the gas bottle can be stored on a boat. On larger craft the usual position is on deck in special vented compartments, but on the smaller boat where space is at a premium the bottles are sometimes hung over the stern on special brackets. Ventilation is directly to the air.

Regulator Valves

The most common LPG used on cruisers is butane which comes in a variety of different sized cylinders. The smaller bottles require a threaded regulator, while the larger bottles use a clip-on regulator valve. A good range of regulators for all sizes of bottle are supplied by Aqua Marine Ltd. Before buying any fittings check the size of your bottle; the larger ones are available with 20mm, 21mm and 27mm fittings.

Alarm Systems

More and more boats now have gas alarm systems fitted because of the peace of mind such a unit provides, this more than justifying their cost. There are some exceptionally efficient gas alarms now available, and most are fitted with very sensitive sensors that trigger the alarm when a gas concentration of only 10 per cent is reached. This percentage of gas is the lowest possible concentration at which there is a risk of an explosion. This means that a leak can be detected before gas, or even petrol fumes for that matter, reach a dangerous level, thereby significantly reducing the risk of an explosion.

Plastimo Ltd produce a very good yet inexpensive alarm and other suppliers can provide more expensive units. Detectors with both an audio and visual alarm are common, but if you feel the need for additional safety some available models incorporate solenoid valves that automatically shut off the gas supply as soon as a leak is discovered.

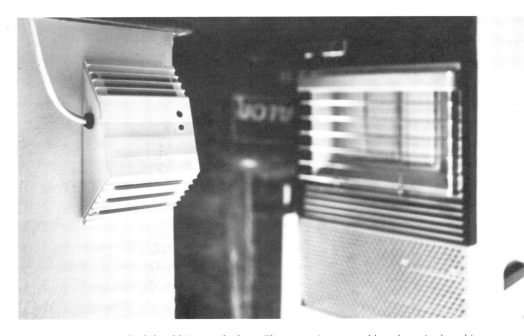

A gas detector is a worthwhile addition to the boat. The sensor is mounted low down in the cabin because LPG is heavier than air and tends to sink into the bilges.

Pipework

Gas pipework should be of the seamless copper type and should be inspected regularly for signs of stress or fatigue, especially at joints and appliances. Make sure that pipes are clipped up at regular intervals (at least every 15 centimetres) and that all joints are visible and accessible. Check a joint's security by using a paintbrush to swab the area with a solution of soapy water. You will soon see if even a small leak is present. Also available is a safe gas-leak detection solution which is contained in a convenient aerosol spray. Sometimes a joint will simply need retightening, but a badly leaking one will need to be replaced. It goes without saying that you must *never* search for a gas leak with a naked flame.

Safety First

When you leave the boat always switch off the gas supply at the main cylinder.

This will take the pressure off the pipework and will reduce the possibility that a joint or valve might leak and cause a build-up of gas in the boat when it is left unattended. When fitting a new system or overhauling an existing one, make sure that each appliance or gas outlet is fitted with its own isolating tap so that that particular section can be closed off. Keep the taps themselves freely movable so that they may be turned off in an emergency.

From a further safety angle, remember that gas heaters and other appliances burn up oxygen within the cabin, and that adequate ventilation must therefore be provided. Apart from leaving a window open, fixed ventilators should be mounted near cookers and behind fridges, and as near as possible to heaters. Some catalytic heaters that are mounted near the floor may be supplied with air from the bilge, the heat drawing up the fresh air. Whichever method you employ, ensure that an adequate, free-moving supply of fresh air is available when using all LPG appliances.

SUMMARY

- The type of gas used aboard pleasure boats is called liquid petroleum gas (LPG) and is a highly volatile substance contained under liquid pressure in a metal cylinder. There are two types: butane and propane.

- In the event of a leak, turn off the gas at the cylinder and open up the hatches or remove floorboards to gain access to the bilge area. Use a plastic bucket to bail out the gas; there really is no better way of removing a large quantity of gas from the bottom of a boat.

- The use of a manual or an automatic change-over system using two bottles avoids the need to search for a spanner and make a physical change-over when the gas supply is exhausted.

- When you leave the boat always switch off the gas supply at the main cylinder. This takes the pressure off the pipework and reduces the risk of a joint or valve leaking and starting a build-up of gas in the boat when it is left unattended.

7
TOILET SYSTEMS

Most boats available today, whether new or second-hand, and from the humblest GRP 'bath tubs' to the most luxurious narrow boats and motor cruisers, have some space allocated within their cabins for the fitting of a toilet and, in some cases, a shower unit. Unlike the early days of pleasure boating when a spade and a roll of soft tissue were the order of the day, today's on-board WC can be a sophisticated, multi-function device incorporating a vast holding tank and freshwater flushing facility, and can even be electrically recharged.

Types of Toilet

Basically, there are four main types of toilet: the portable chemical type, commonly called the 'bucket 'n' chuck it'; the pump-out system, popular on hire boats and featuring a special holding tank for the collection of sewage; sea toilets which discharge the waste directly below water-level; and recirculatory toilets. Out of all these types I can think of none which is based on or similar to a domestic toilet – the ones in the first and last categories are usually found on small boats and caravans, and those in the second and third categories have usually been specifically designed for marine use, and are therefore slightly miniaturized and fitted with corrosion-free stainless steel bronze or alloy fittings.

I will now take a brief look at each type, detailing the various functions and accessories available and examining the suitability of each toilet for use on a variety of inland, estuarine and seagoing craft.

Chemical Toilets

One of the simpler toilets in this category consists of a plastic container, like a bucket, which is usually surrounded by an exterior housing with seat fixed to it. A sewage break-down chemical is added proportionally to water and placed in the bottom of the bucket. As the container fills, a solution of water and chemical must be added until the toilet becomes full; it is then a matter of carrying the whole thing to the nearest sanitary point for emptying and refilling with fresh chemical. These toilets are usually fine as long as the chemical is changed regularly and the toilet emptied frequently; otherwise unpleasant smells may result.

More sophisticated chemical toilets are available, and these have a separate 'holding' tank underneath and a fresh-water supply above. The chemical solution is added to the bottom tank and the fresh water is flushed into the bowl by using a special set of bellows at the back of the seat. Once full, the holding tank is separated from the top seat unit by means of a lever and can then be carried away

One of the most popular chemical toilets, the Port Potti has a holding tank for waste which can be removed for disposal. A freshwater tank on top can be used to flush the toilet in the usual way.

cleanly and simply for emptying. A range of such toilets is available, the main difference between them being the number of flushes per tank of water. Chemical toilets are usually fitted in small GRP cruisers and are sometimes used on larger craft if a second toilet compartment is available.

Pump-Out Toilets

More popular on canals and river boats, the pump-out system is both clean and efficient. It utilizes a large-capacity holding tank where the sewage is stored and has a freshwater supply for flushing. Once the tank is full – on a boat with one toilet and a crew of six, this normally takes about a week – the boat is taken along to the nearest boat-yard that has pump-out facilities. A special pump is then con-

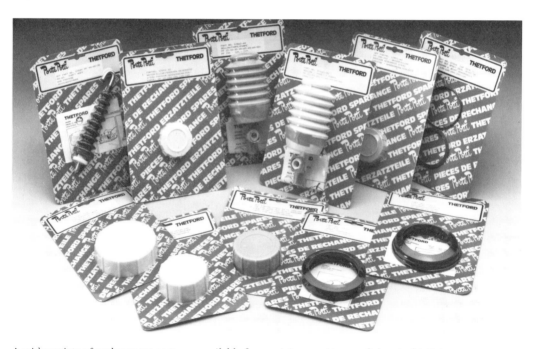

A wide variety of replacement parts are available for servicing most types of chemical toilet.

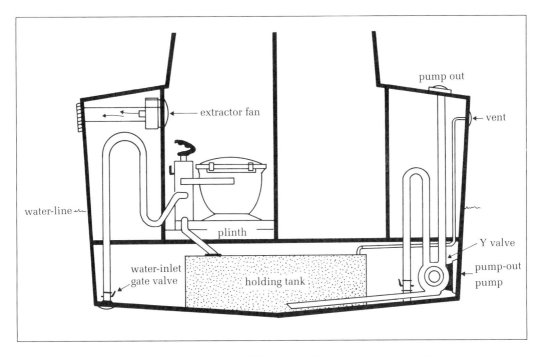

A schematic diagram of a toilet system using a holding tank. This system is very popular as it is environmentally friendly. The waste is stored in the tank ready to be sucked out by a special pump-out machine at a boat-yard. Water for flushing is drawn in from the sea, river or canal through the water-inlet gate valve.

nected to a skin fitting, usually on the gunwale or roof of the boat, and the sewage is removed by suction to a storage tank. The boat's system is recharged with a mixture of sanitary fluid and water through the same skin fitting.

One of the beauties of this system is that the tanks can be made specially to fit the available space allocated in your toilet compartment. The toilet, usually a ceramic bowl, sits atop the tank and has a lever or lift hand pump with which to flush it; some even have a position for a wet or dry bowl – the former leaves water in the toilet while the latter leaves it dry.

For craft which also cruise off shore, an adaptation of the pump-out system includes an additional outlet on the holding tank which is connected to a macerator pump. The pump is then connected to a sea cock in the bottom of the boat and is used to pump out the holding tank when at sea. At the end of each season the tank and system should be flushed through thoroughly and disinfected to ensure that it is fresh and clean for the following season, and also to ensure that no salt corrosion can take place. An air vent is required in the holding tank to prevent odours blowing back up through the toilet, and, in the event of the holding tank becoming overfilled, to prevent it from emptying into the bilges. The outlet should be kept well away from the cockpit and any air intakes or windows for obvious reasons!

Sea Toilets

The sea toilet is hardly ever seen on inland waterways because health and safety rulings forbid the discharge of sewage over the side or directly into the canal or river. Many of the boats that use this very popular system are cruised off shore or in estuaries.

Mainly designed for use where space is at a premium, sea toilets are normally fitted to a plinth above the water-line. A system of valves and sea cocks is used with a pump – hand or electrically operated – to flush the sewage out into the sea and to pump in sea water for flushing. These units require much more thought and time to install than a more conventional WC, and are usually more expensive because of the need for bronze sea cocks, extra piping and special valves. A wide variety is available and you will usually find them on board larger cruisers and motor yachts – sometimes with two in tandem. However, in these environmentally aware times, careful thought should be given before fitting this type.

Recirculatory Toilets

The recirculatory lavatory was for years known as a 'Broads' toilet because it is widely used in hire cruisers on the Norfolk Broads. Usually square in shape, they are built into the compartment and use a single charge of chemical-impregnated water – normally around 40–45 litres (9–10 gallons) – which continues to recirculate each time the bowl is flushed. A hinged flap at the base of the bowl keeps odours down to a minimum, and you can always tell when the toilet needs servicing as the flap dips down into the liquid. Various sizes can be bought

and quotes are available from most boat-yards which offer a fitting service. The method of emptying and recharging is similar to that of a pump-out toilet, but they can become rather smelly – especially in hot weather!

Installation

Whichever type of toilet is chosen, it is important that it is installed securely. In rough weather the toilet may have to withstand considerable strain when being subjected to the weight of an adult who is rolling with the motion of the boat. All but the most primitive types have some sort of fixing device for keeping the toilet in position, and this should be checked before you buy it; if it cannot be secured properly it will be unsuitable for sea going use. Chemical toilets often use a bracket which is screwed to the floor of the toilet compartment, to which the toilet can be clipped and unclipped for emptying. Holding-tank toilets, like normal sea toilets, are usually bolted down as permanent fixtures.

As many toilets are built to be extremely compact and are therefore rather too low for comfort, it is usually necessary to build a plinth on which they can be placed. Depending on the room available, the best way to get the toilet at the most comfortable level is to first measure the height of the toilet in your home from floor to seat top. This will be the ideal comfortable height, but as it may be too high for toilet compartments with limited headroom a compromise must be made to achieve the optimum height in the space available. The plinth itself is a simple item to construct, being little more than a box which is bolted to the floor. Timbers

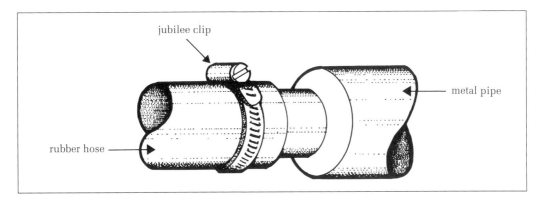

The only sure way of connecting a rubber hose to a metal one is to use a jubilee-type clip.

measuring 5 × 2.5cm (2 × 1in) are adequate for the frame, while an exterior-grade ply will give a firm base on to which the toilet can be fitted.

Extractor Fan

While working on the toilet compartment, it is well worth the extra cost to fit an extractor fan in the area. A car heater fan from your breaker's yard can be used for maximum economy, although there are many excellent fans available from chandlers. The outlet to the fan from the compartment should be fairly high up, but the exact position will depend on the layout. The fan can be vented out through a small stainless steel louvre vent just below the gunwale or through the cabin side above deck level. For the little extra work and cost involved it will prevent a build-up of unpleasant odours.

Sea Cocks

The inlet and outlet cocks for sea and holding-tank toilets are usually standard sizes: 12mm (½in) and 25mm (1in). Naturally, it is easiest to fit these with the

boat ashore, but it is possible to do the job by arranging for the boat to be heeled over on one side so that the sea cocks can be fitted below the water-line. Obviously, the sea cocks should be placed as deep as can be arranged, with the inlet cock lower down and aft of the outlet. Heavy weights lined up along the side-deck will often be

Two toilet sea cocks removed from the boat and dismantled for servicing and greasing. Obviously this job will have to be done while the boat is slipped from the water.

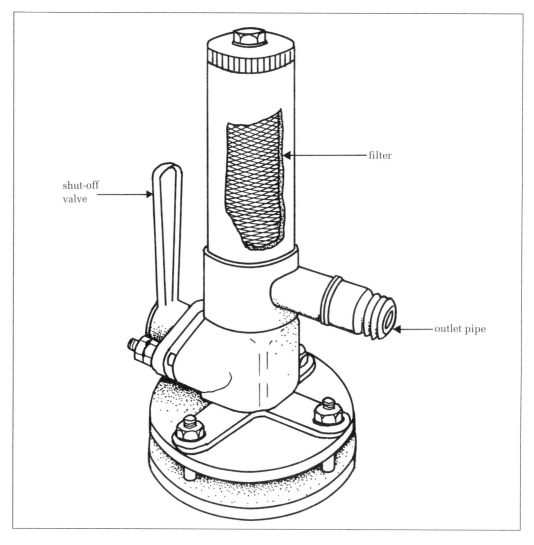

A cut-away diagram of a standard sea cock, showing the filter element, shut-off valve and outlet pipe. (Courtesy of Perkins Engines.)

sufficient to heel the boat over far enough for the work to be completed.

Holes for the sea cocks are best cut using a hole saw of the correct size to suit the sea-cock spigot. An electric drill makes the job very quick, but if it is being done with the boat afloat and heeled over it is essential to have an earth leakage circuit breaker (RCCB) in the line to prevent potentially lethal electric shocks while working close to the water. On steel boats the hole saw will need to be of a type suitable for cutting metal and the drill speed should be as slow as possible –

around 400rpm or less for a 2.5cm (1in) hole. A cutting compound on the saw teeth will also speed up the process and give the hole saw a longer life. Once the hole is of the correct size it should be protected with the same paint as used for the rest of the underwater area, then the sea cock should be bedded down well with a suitable sealant. There are now two types: one for GRP craft and one for all other materials.

Pipework from sea cocks must be arranged so that it comes up in a loop above the water-line before connecting to the toilet or holding tank. For the inlet this is to ensure that a quantity of water will remain in the bottom of the bowl or, if the toilet is below the water-line, to prevent water syphoning in and overflowing from the toilet or the holding tank. All pipework should be run in reinforced flexible hose so that there is no danger of its collapsing because of suction from the pumps.

Any underwater sea cock needs to be of the best possible materials as it is, in effect, a hole in the bottom of the boat. If it is a cheap brass unit as used for domestic plumbing it could soon lose its zinc content and collapse, causing the boat to sink very rapidly – probably when you have left it unattended during the week. Gunmetal is the normal material for reliable sea cocks and, although fairly expensive, is worth it for the peace of mind it provides. Other suitable materials are silicon bronze, aluminium bronze and nickel aluminium bronze, all of which are very corrosion resistant.

On steel craft it is good practice to site a small anode near the sea cocks to minimize any electrolytic corrosion which may be set up on the steel of the hull by the superior quality of the sea cocks.

A range of ceramic, fully-flushing sea toilets.

Maintenance

The toilet should be serviced occasionally to keep it working efficiently. There is nothing quite as bad as a broken toilet – especially on a long sea passage! Some boats fitted with simple chemical toilets require only regular emptying and re-charging with the correct solution of chemical fluid and water for flushing. Holding-tank toilets have a special tank, usually installed under the toilet itself, which is used to store the waste until it can be pumped out at a marina or water-side pump-out station. A machine sucks out the waste, replacing it with fresh water and chemical solution. Some of these toilets can be discharged overboard at sea, although in these environmentally aware times this practice is not recommended.

All toilets will benefit from an oc-casional rinse through with a mild disin-fectant, but harsh bleaching disinfectants should be avoided as the strength of the concentrate can damage the valve seals (this applies to both chemical and holding-tank toilets). Toilets with hand pumps can become very stiff to operate after a short period of time; a good way to lubricate these is either to pour a little cooking oil or to spray some wax furni-ture polish into the bowl and pump it through. The difference this makes to the action of the pump is amazing. Additionally, the shaft of the hand pump can be smeared lightly with the same lubricant to give a smooth stroke.

Any moving parts of the toilet will benefit from an occasional squirt of a light lubricant oil, and the exterior surfaces of the toilet can be cleaned in the same manner as those of a toilet at home.

SUMMARY

- Unlike the early days of pleasure boating when a spade and a roll of soft tissue were the order of the day, today's on-board WC can be a sophisticated, multi-function device incorporating a vast holding tank and freshwater flushing facility, and can even be electrically recharged.

- Popular on canals and rivers, the pump-out system is both clean and efficient. It utilizes a large-capacity holding tank where the sewage is stored and has a freshwater supply for flushing.

- The sea toilet is hardly ever seen on inland waterways because health and safety rulings forbid the discharge of sewage over the side or directly into the canal or river. Many of the boats that use this very popular system are cruised off shore or in estuaries.

- Whichever type of toilet is chosen, it is important that it is installed securely. In rough weather the toilet may have to withstand considerable strain when being subjected to the weight of an adult who is rolling with the motion of the boat.

- The toilet should be serviced occasionally to keep it working efficiently. There is nothing quite as bad as a broken toilet – especially on a long sea passage!

8
HEATING SYSTEMS

The rising cost of boats and their equipment means that more owners want to have the maximum amount of cruising time for their investment. Extending the usable season of a boat from the usual Easter to October period has one disadvantage in some regions – the weather! However, with the availability of several workable and efficient heating systems on the market, extending the cruising season to the whole year is now both practical and possible.

Boat heaters come in various sizes and outputs, some using diesel, others using paraffin or liquid petroleum gas and some – usually those fitted in canal narrow boats – even using solid fuel. Of these types, it is often essential to have an external flue for exhaust gases in addition to an adequate flow of air within the boat itself.

Choice of Heater

You must first make the decision as to whether you would like the whole boat to be warm or whether heat in just one cabin will be adequate. There are some simple and inexpensive heaters which will warm one cabin quite well, and this may be enough for a small boat. However, if you have a family-sized boat with several cabins you will probably need heat in all of them. This means either a separate heater in each cabin, or a single central-heating system with an effective means of circulating the heat right around the boat. Single heaters in every cabin usually end up being expensive, even if the heaters themselves are quite cheap, because you will need a fuel supply to each cabin and also some means of getting rid of the exhaust fumes from each cabin.

Central Heating

Apart from catalytic heaters and some solid-fuel heaters, there are two popular types of central-heating system for boats: the ducted warm-air type and the small-bore hot-water type with a radiator in each cabin. These work on the same principles as domestic central-heating systems, except that all the equipment has to be built for use in a marine environment. With both types of system, it is vital that a reasonably powerful motor is used to drive either the fan or the pump so that the heat is circulated effectively, and this is reflected in both the initial cost of the heater and of the battery drain. Unfortunately, there is no way round the rule that the less powerful the motor, the less effective the heat distribution.

Fuel Type

The next decision to be made is the type

A small, mobile heater running on Camping Gaz is ideal for larger cabins. However, as the heater is mounted on wheels, this type of fire should not be used when the boat is under way.

of fuel you wish to use. The three most common types are diesel, paraffin and gas, with diesel and paraffin being much cheaper. In addition, there is the fundamental fact that gas is easy to ignite but diesel is not. This means inevitably that diesel heaters are more complicated to use than gas heaters because you must go through a complex procedure to get the diesel to burn. However, many boat owners feel that this is not a drawback, and that the less gas they have aboard the better. Gas systems and applications can

be a serious hazard if they are not carefully installed (*see* Chapter 6, page 61).

Inexpensive heating systems dispense with the exhaust flue, and rely on exhaust gases escaping through open windows or ventilators in the same way as fumes from the cooker. Providing that windows are left open there is not much danger of carbon-monoxide poisoning, but obviously the water vapour created by combustion (with an open-flame heater) or oxidation (in the case of a catalytic heater) means that the boat will remain damp on

On traditional canal boats these cast-iron solid-fuel stoves are very popular. They can burn timber, coal, coke or smokeless fuel.

The Webasto diesel boat heater can be supplied with a kit designed for those who like to do it themselves. The unit has an output of 2.3kW and is ideal for boats around 30 feet in length.

The interior workings of an Ardic central-heating unit shows the main burner, ignition controls and hot-air outlet pipe.

humid days. However, such systems do provide some warmth so are effective on cold, dry days. They also provide value for money since the cost of installation is so low. Of the two types, catalytic heaters are much safer than open-flame radiant heaters, the latter being a significant fire hazard.

Unless your boat is moored in a marina with a shore-based electricity supply, virtually every sensible form of heating available works by burning some sort of hydrocarbon fuel – either solid, liquid or gas. Some owners are enthusiastic about solid-fuel stoves, but most owners will not be happy carrying hot ashes through the cabin to dispose of them or stoking the

stove manually. For most owners, the choice therefore lies between diesel, paraffin or gas (propane or butane).

All the better quality heaters have some sort of exhaust flue so that the exhaust gases are vented outside the boat, but on a seagoing boat the exhaust flue is an expensive part of the installation. Since the fuel consists largely of carbon and hydrogen, the heat is created by chemical reaction and takes place at a relatively low temperature. This means that a much safer heater can be built, but the actual chemical reaction is exactly the same as that which takes place when solid fuel burns. The water vapour in the exhaust fumes, although harmless, obviously adds

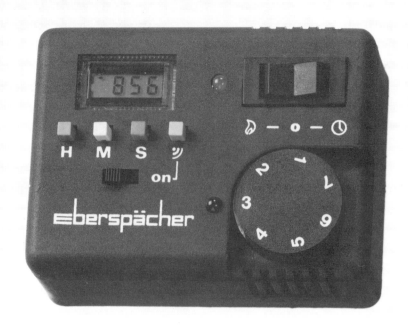

An all-in-one timer/alarm and thermostat unit of the Eberspacher ducted-air central-heating system.

to one of the least attractive features of boat heating systems.

Warm-Air Heaters

Modern warm-air heaters all work on a similar basic principle, whereby an electric fan inducts clear air and forces it over a multiple-fin heat exchanger and then out into the cabins via a ducting system. In effect, the heat exchanger is a small oil-fired heater with its own combustion air inlet and exhaust vent. The result is that warm, dry air is circulated throughout the cabin whilst the exhaust gases of the heat exchanger are released via a vented flue. The temperature is controlled with a cabin thermostat; some systems also include individual cabin on/off switches and 24-hour preselection timers.

SUMMARY

- With the availability of several workable and efficient heating systems on the market, extending the cruising season to the whole year is now both possible and practical.

- Boat heaters come in various sizes and outputs, some using diesel, others using paraffin or LPG, and some even using solid fuel.

- Apart from catalytic heaters and some solid-fuel heaters, there are two popular types of central-heating system for boats: the ducted warm-air type and the small-bore hot-water type with a radiator in each cabin.

- Unless your boat is moored in a marina with a shore-based electricity supply, virtually every sensible form of heating available works by burning some sort of hydrocarbon fuel – either solid, liquid or gas.

9
STEERING AND CONTROL SYSTEMS

It is pointless having a first-class engine to power your cruiser if you are always having difficulty with the throttle or if the gearshift fails at a vital moment. The value of a solid, reliable steering- and power-unit control system speaks for itself. How many times have you heard of an accident or breakdown when the trouble was traced to a failed steering column or broken control cables which were installed incorrectly?

Control systems used to be much simpler than they are today: in the case of small boats, they probably consisted of a

The essence of a good helm position, a wheel at a comfortable height with throttle/gearshift readily to hand.

The steering system for a single outboard mounted in an outboard well. The motor is steered by a rod attached to the central bracket, whilst throttle and gearshift is done through Morse-type cables.

single-lever control box and wheel-operated cable and pulley steering. Nowadays, with advances in technology and materials, many more systems are available: dual-circuit stations with an identical set of controls situated on the flybridge of a boat, hydraulic rudder control, chain-link steering and automatic trimming of engines and boat hulls. There are also many makes of automatic pilot available for the small pleasure boat which help reduce the strain of steering a vessel on long sea passages. There are several suppliers of steering and control equipment, some of the better-known ones feature a wide range of equipment for all types of boat, up to and including

lengths of 50 feet and more. There are many different options and combinations, and the choice really depends upon the type and length of boat, the size and type of engine (inboard or outboard), and the conditions in which the boat is used.

Basic Installation

In its simplest form, a basic installation is made up of a double push-pull cable (one cable for the throttle and one for the gearshift), a single- or dual-lever control box, a steering cable, a wheel and operating gear. Teleflex use a simple set of calculations which enable the owner to

The steering position on an open GRP fishing boat. The wheel is mounted on a cuddy console which allows the owner to custom fit his own instruments. The throttle/gear lever is well placed on the gunwale for ease of co-ordination when steering.

order the correct length of cable for his steering and control cables. Distance A is measured from the centre of the wheel to the gunwale, B from the dashboard to the transom and C from the gunwale to the transom centre. You then subtract 100mm (4in) for each 90-degree bend (*see* diagram opposite). Using this method saves both time and money, and also prevents you from ordering either too short or too long a cable.

When it comes to throttle and gearshift cables, the location of the operating box should first be decided upon. It should be in a comfortable position for the seated helmsman, not too far forward and not too high up. The distance is then measured from this box along the shortest unobstructed route to the engine's gearbox and throttle actuator. Bends in the cable should not be more than 200mm (8in)

maximum radius and the length of each ready-made cable should be calculated from rod end to rod end. Take care when choosing your route – do not trap the cables beneath floorboards or around bulkhead supports and, if installing for an outboard motor, allow a couple of extra feet for the loop outside the engine.

There are many different attachments available to match the rod ends of the control cables to most of the major manufacturer's engines both inboard or outboard. When you order these, state the boat's engine size, type and, if possible, its year of manufacture. Some manufacturers supply their own terminations with the engine but check with your control-cable stockist to see if these will work on the cables you intend to buy.

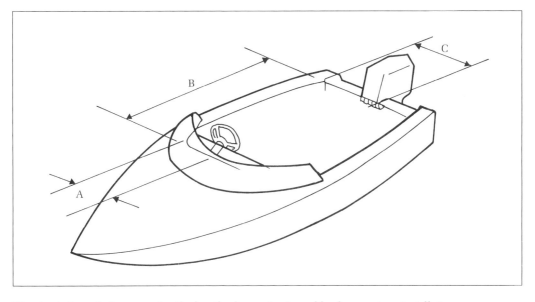

The simple formula for measuring the length of your steering cables for any given installation on a small motor boat.

Over the years, automatic pilots have become more streamlined. This Navico Powerpilot comprises ram, control box and actuator control.

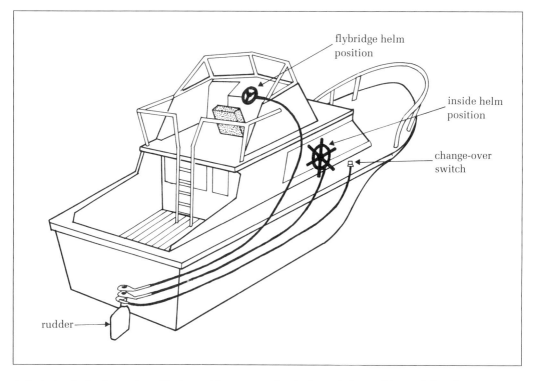

A dual-circuit steering system. The two cable runs, one for the lower helm position and the other for the flying bridge, can be changed over using a special switch. Some systems now have automatic change-over.

Dual-Circuit Systems

Many larger motor cruisers with a flybridge have the facility for a second helm position. Specialist steering and control systems are available for these, with dual circuits for throttle and gearshift and a second steering wheel. Most people choose to fit the sort that can be used from only one position at a time as this prevents interference and is much safer. You can choose from several remote exchanger mechanisms which are lever operated. The handle is pulled out and turned to disengage one station and lock in the other, but many systems these days are self-disengaging.

The advantages of flybridge steering may not readily be apparent to some. Apart from the fact that you will be out of doors in hot weather, the ability of the flybridge to give all-round visibility when coming into narrow channels or difficult marinas is a boon. Careful practice with the twin-lever throttle and gears makes steering the boat and manoeuvring it into tight berths child's play – in some instances you may not even have to touch the wheel.

The helm position on the flying bridge of a large ocean-going motor boat. Repeater gauges for most of the engine instruments duplicate those below, but a second compass has been installed as well as controls for trim tabs and outdrive leg.

A plush steering position on a sports cruiser. It all looks very impressive, but how difficult will it be to operate some of those buttons through the spokes of the steering wheel?

The throttle setting and gear change on many engines are controlled by a single lever. The cables are linked together below the box, and pushing the lever forward engages both forward gear and opens the throttle.

Maintenance

Many new cruisers come supplied with an engine and will therefore have the steering and control gear already fitted – hopefully by a competent mechanic. However, this does not entirely absolve the owner from any further association with it as the gear requires examination and maintenance in the same way as the engine and electrical systems.

At each engine service, or when preparing the boat for a new cruising season, check the linkages at the gearbox and throttle. The cable terminations should also be smeared lightly with waterproof grease or light machine oil. Check the cotter pins and attachment for wear. At the control box end these can usually be split and the nylon inserts and cable rod ends greased. Check for any wear on the centre 'stop' for the neutral gear position, and when reassembling see that the mounting bolts are tight and that no surrounding GRP or timber is splitting. Steering gear is sometimes quite difficult to remove and access, so unless there is excessive play at the wheel it is best to leave it well alone.

The rudder hangings should be inspected for wear, as should the rudder post, gland packing, bearings and pintals. Is the tiller arm tight, with just the right amount of play? Are the sacrificial anodes (if fitted) worn away? If so, replace them. Remember that the rudder is as important as the engine itself – without it you cannot possibly steer the boat. If in doubt about any part of its gear and operation, seek the advice of a professional boat-yard. On the inside of the hull check the security of the steering-cable clamp on the transom, grease the exposed part of the inner core and look for signs of wear in the ball and socket or retaining pin which attaches the cable to the rudder actuator.

Controls for Open Inflatables

A major problem facing the lone boatman with his light inflatable craft and relatively heavy outboard-motor power unit is one of bow lift. This is a problem that occurs when the occupant of the boat sits at the stern, steering the boat using the tiller attached to the outboard when the craft is under power. The thrust of the motor

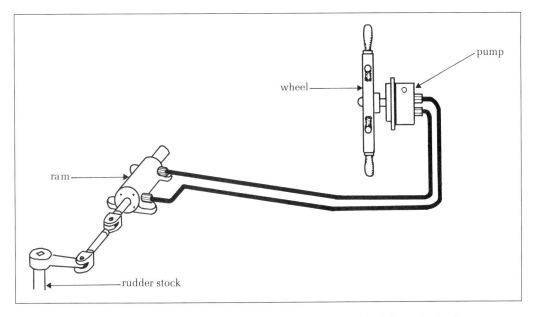

A simple hydraulic steering system. Turning the wheel operates a pump which forces hydraulic fluid through the pipes, in turn moving a ram connected to the boat's rudder.

When installing a hydraulic steering system always allow access to the rear of the steering wheel, an area where many of the hydraulic lines converge. This one has a useful removable panel which also gives access to the electrics.

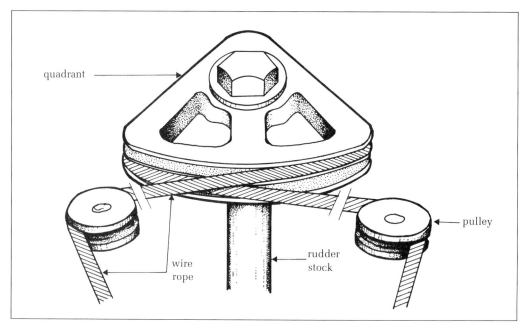

Older craft might still have quadrant steering where a wire hawser or rope is passed around pulleys and a shaped quadrant attached to the rudder stock.

On hydraulic steering, top up the fluid to the correct level at the reservoir. The large central nut can be removed for this purpose.

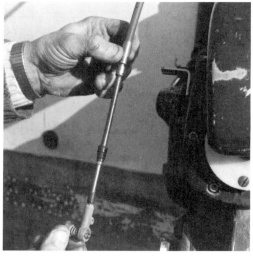

When servicing control cables make sure that you check the terminating ends. This is the spot that gets most wear. It should be greased on a regular basis and any cotter pins should be examined for signs of fracture.

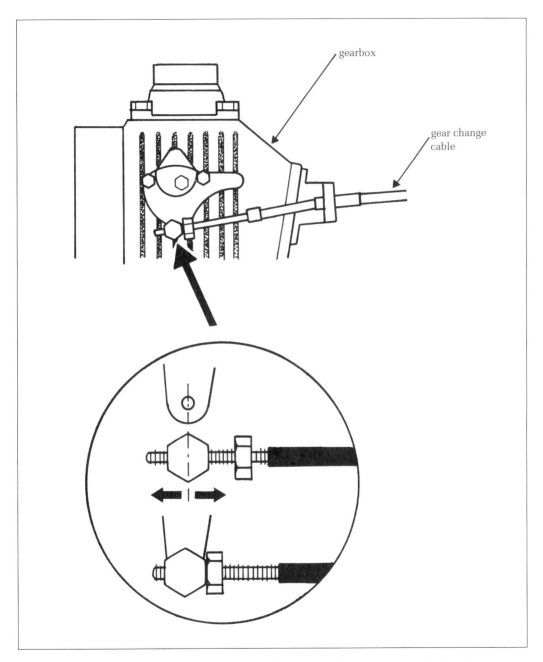

When maintaining steering and control cables, check the points at which they are attached to the engine and gearbox. Light greasing will help to keep movement smooth and trouble-free.

combined with the weight of the boater unbalances the boat and raises the bows. This not only feels uncomfortable and unstable, but it can be downright dangerous in the event that a freak gust of wind lifts the bows even further and eventually flips over the entire boat.

A special steering system fitted to the bottom boards of an inflatable will alleviate the above problem by allowing the boat's single occupant to sit further forward, so regaining the lost balance and achieving stability once more. After deciding upon the length of cables you require for the main steering as well as throttle and gear change, and determining the best position for the steering column according to any inflatable or solid thwarts that may be fitted to your particular boat, the base plate is simply placed on the appropriate spot and the positions of the four fixing holes marked through with a pencil. The holes are then drilled and cleaned up before the plate is bolted in place. Use rustproof bolts for this purpose. I would use four galvanized roofing bolts with large, smooth, rounded heads – the floor of your boat may have an inflatable keel running up it, so you don't want sharp projections.

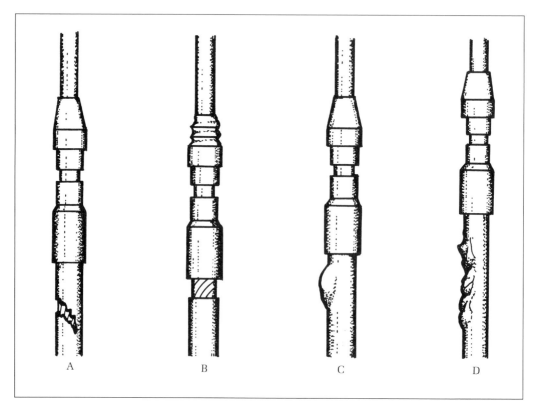

Various problems which can occur to the ends of throttle and gear-change cables: (a) cut or cracked jacket; (b) separation of the jacket; (c) corrosion under the jacket; (d) a burnt or melted jacket.

Check the ball coupling where the steering cable is fixed to the outboard bracket, greasing it occasionally and wiping away any corrosion.

Ensure that the plate is square when you mark it out and see that it is fitted the right way around – with the four supporting cradles facing forwards. The centre column, complete with the steering box, wheel, throttle and gear-change levers and their associated cables, may now be attached to the base plate using the four clamp plates and turn-down screws. The control cables are simply routed either along the top or tucked below one of the boat's inflatable sponsons before being coupled to the outboard.

The steering-cable ball joint is attached to the outboard carrying handle either in the vertical or horizontal position depending upon the placement of the hole. The cable is attached to the ball by sliding back the outer sleeve, slotting the cable over the ball and repositioning the outer sleeve over the joint. These joints should

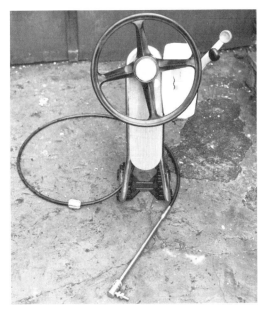

One of the special inflatable boat steering columns. Simply designed, it comes complete with wheel and cables for throttle, gearshift and steering.

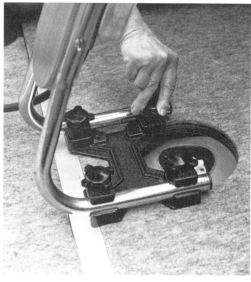

Marking out the position for the steering column base plate on the bottom boards of the inflatable.

The column is simply tightened down on to the plate by hand. Large screws are used so that the column can be disassembled after use when the boat is packed into the boot of a car.

The steering column in position. Cables can be routed away down the sides of the boat. It might help the steerer to have a small seat – perhaps use a plank of wood – available for comfortable steering.

also be greased periodically with a suitable waterproof grease.

The transom fixing for the steering cable is equally simple in its installation. Depending upon the type of system chosen, a ball-jointed bracket is bolted to the transom, once again using nonferrous screws or bolts, and the clamp is bolted securely to the outboard end of the cable.

Throttle and gear cables are routed and attached to your outboard in the usual way, depending upon the type of termination and fixing applicable to your particular motor. There are several types of steering and control system available for inflatable and folding craft, many of them supplied along with the boat – especially boats with a rigid hull made of glass-fibre.

Engine Instruments

The engine's instruments are its eyes and ears, telling you the state of your engine from its operating temperature to the amount of fuel in the tank. They are vital to safe cruising and should always be looked after. From time to time you may have to replace one or two of your engine instruments: they may be too old to function accurately or you may be replacing the engine with a new or second-hand model and want new instruments to go with it.

Engine-instrument systems can be as simple or as complex as you like. I have seen small sports boats with even smaller dash consoles which looked like the flight deck of an aircraft, and big seagoing cruisers with twin engines and every add-

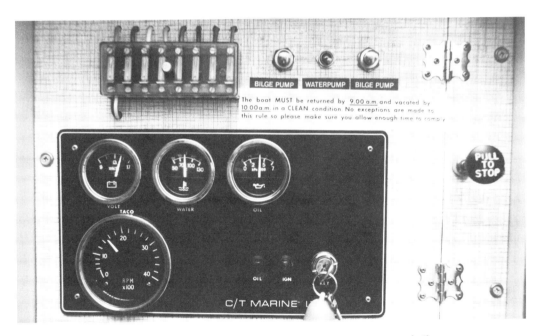

A basic instrument panel comprising tachometer, fuel gauge, water temperature and oil-pressure gauge, along with an oil warning light and an ignition light and key starter. Note also the handy position of the main electrical fuses.

on device you could think of whose instrument panel was the size of the proverbial postage stamp! However, there are a few basic instruments that are essential and these are dealt with in the remainder of this chapter. They form the simplest of layouts and will monitor all the important engine functions.

Starter Mechanism

Even if your engine has a pull cable for stopping it, it is highly likely that it has a key-start mechanism. In its basic form, the turn of the key sends an electrical current to the starter solenoid which in turn switches over to carry the much heavier current required for the starter motor to turn over the engine. On a diesel unit, a spring-loaded section on the start switch allows a preheat current to warm up the fuel-heater circuit. You normally hold this on 'heat' for anything up to 30 seconds (more on a cold morning) until the engine fires. Such mechanisms are simply installed through an appropriate sized hole and are held in place with a rear nut. They rarely go wrong, but a general check of contacts and a spray with a waterproofing agent every season will help keep corrosion at bay.

Generator Light

This lights up the moment you turn the key to start the engine. It indicates that power is available from the battery to start the engine. Once started, the light should go out and stay out while the engine is running.

If the light comes on when the engine seems to be running normally, this indicates either a broken alternator belt or that there is a fault somewhere in the generator or its circuitry, in which case the engine should be stopped immediately and the fault traced. Replacement of the bulb or its holder is a simple matter of removing the dash and taking off the single holding nut.

Oil-Pressure Indicator

This is one of the most important instrument gauges as it monitors the oil levels and the pressure of the fluid during its transit around the engine itself. If your system is fitted with a gauge, the pressure will read either in bars or in pounds per square inch. When you first acquire the engine find out exactly what the normal oil pressure is. Once you have been cruising for a while, you will soon come to remember this figure as well as noting where the needle normally rests on the dial.

Generally, the correct pressure of a system should be in the region of about 4 bars or 50–60lb/sq in. Any deviation from this during engine operation might indicate a loss of oil from the engine, a level that has not been topped up or blocked oil passages in the engine itself. The engine should be stopped instantly as running on low oil pressure can have a devastating effect. A lack of oil will cause serious damage to big ends, bearings and rods, and could seize the engine solid. You should therefore always keep an eye on the gauge.

Temperature Indicator

This is an essential indicator. Usually a gauge in design, the gradations may be in degrees Celsius or Fahrenheit, or a combination of the two. As with the oil pressure, you should know your working

An example of a standard engine instrument. This one is a temperature gauge which is attached to its sender. In turn, the sender is screwed into the engine block where it measures the temperature.

temperature and keep a careful eye on it when using the boat.

If the temperature starts to climb above the normal reading it may be for a variety of reasons. Your flow of coolant may have been interrupted by a leak from a split hose, a burnt-out water-pump impeller or by a loss of water into the bilge. If you have only just recommissioned the craft after winter lay-up, the cooling-water intake valve may still be shut. The inlet could also have become blocked by mud, silt or plastic bags. Once again, the action is to close down the engine and find the source of the problem.

Fuel Computer

Most boat operators will admit that the least reliable item of equipment on their vessel is the fuel gauge. For several reasons the vehicle-derived fuel gauge is not suited to the marine environment, not least because of the often violent motion of the boat when at sea which makes an accurate reading impossible to achieve. An altogether better alternative is to have a fuel computer which monitors fuel consumption and keeps a tally of fuel used. This makes it easy to calculate the amount of petrol remaining in the tank and therefore the vessel's range.

Fuel computers for petrol-engine boats are easy to install as they simply consist of a flow sensor in the fuel line connected to a control unit which calculates the signals from the sensor and turns them into a visual display. The problem with diesel engines is that they need a fuel leak-off back to the tank to return the excess fuel which is delivered by the lift pump. This obviously complicates matters as much more fuel passes the flow sensor than is actually burned in the engine.

One solution to this problem is to fit flow sensors to both feed and return, and to use micro-chip technology to subtract one from the other before displaying the result. The problem with this system is that any inaccuracies within the flow sensors are immediately doubled, and further inaccuracies during calculation of flow and return can only make matters worse. However, one company has taken an altogether different path, and instead of using two flow sensors it has designed a system which not only gives accurate fuel consumption measurements but also makes the system constantly self-bleeding. This means that even drastic air leaks in the fuel system will be unlikely to stop the engine, while at the same time the fuel is cooled for greater efficiency. This system therefore not only offers fuel consumption data and fuel cooling but the added safety factor of air-free fuel for greater reliability. These additional advantages make the unit worth considering even without the fuel-consumption computer – the air bleed/fuel cooler is, in fact, available as a stand alone automatic air-bleed unit if required (*see* below).

Bleeder/Cooler Unit

The system works by routing the fuel through the air bleeder/cooler unit. Ideally, the cooler unit should be mounted off the engine in a convenient position to minimize additional fuel piping. The cooler consists of two vertical tubes mounted side by side which are heavily finned for maximum cooling, and should ideally be located in an area of cool air flow. There is a connection at the bottom of each tube and, as both tubes can be used, the most convenient should be chosen for the fuel inlet.

A T fitting is situated between the flow sensor and the cooler unit, and this is how the system manages to avoid having a fuel return back to the tank. The return is fed back into the fuel inlet via the T and therefore forms a closed circuit. The original return feed to the tank is connected to the top of the cooler unit simply as a precautionary measure in case the air bleed valve should ever leak and allow fuel to pass. In the unlikely event of this happening, the excess fuel is simply returned to the tank in the usual manner and the engine runs completely normally. The only indication that a leak has

occurred is an apparent sharp increase in fuel consumption as registered on the computer display. Referring to the schematic diagram below, fuel is taken from the tank through the sedimenter via the lift pump, then through the first fine filter and non-return valve into the flow sensor. From here it passes through the T and up one tube of the air bleed/fuel cooler to where the air bleed valve is situated. Any air present in the fuel is removed via the air bleeder at this point. The fuel then passes down through the other tube where it is fed to the injection pump and finally to the injectors. Excess fuel is returned via the T to the inlet side of the fuel cooler.

The fuel system beyond the lift pump is maintained at a fairly constant pressure as the tank leak-off return is effectively sealed to fuel, although any air passes freely from the system and back to the tank via the air bleeder. Fuel leaks in the pressure side of the system are easy to find, and the chance of the engine's suffering from an air-induced stoppage from leaks on the suction side are virtually nil as the air bleed valve will pass vast amounts of air without affecting the engine's performance.

Memory

The fuel computer unit incorporates an LED display with push-buttons for selecting either fuel consumption or fuel used. The memory will retain the fuel-used readings even when the unit is switched off, as the memory circuit bypasses the on-off switch and can be supplied directly from the fuse board. If all battery power is shut off the reading will revert to zero, but it is a simple matter to maintain a 'fuel used' log to record the last reading before the power was shut off. Many commercial craft maintain a permanent memory feed which bypasses the battery master switches so that memory is constantly available.

The unit can be used to discover the optimum throttle setting for maximum fuel economy simply by altering the throttle setting and watching the effect that this has on the fuel being used. It can be an eye-opening experience to find that a drop of half a knot in speed can gain an improvement of 2 litres (half a gallon) an hour in fuel consumption.

SUMMARY

- The value of a solid, reliable steering- and power-unit control system speaks for itself. How many times have you heard of an accident or breakdown when the trouble was traced to a failed steering column or broken control cables which were installed incorrectly.

- At each engine service, or when preparing the boat for a new cruising season, check the linkages at the gearbox and throttle. The cable terminations should also be smeared lightly with waterproof grease or light machine oil.

- A special steering system fitted to the bottom boards of an inflatable boat will alleviate the problem of bow lift by allowing the boat's single occupant to sit further forward, so regaining the lost balance and achieving stability once more.

- The engine's instruments are its eyes and ears, telling you the state of your engine from its operating temperature to the amount of fuel in the tank. They are vital to safe cruising and should always be looked after.

- An alternative to the fuel gauge is the fuel computer, which monitors fuel consumption and keeps a tally of fuel used. This makes it easy to calculate the amount of petrol remaining in the tank and therefore the vessel's range.

10
DECK FITTINGS

The outside areas of a motorboat – usually termed 'on-deck' – have several sections of equipment which are examined in this chapter. Although not coming under a general term, fittings such as cleats, fairleads, windows, bollards, mooring points, winches and the deck surface itself, need careful treatment both in terms of safety and durability when the boat is in use. Loose fittings can be extremely dangerous and on occasion have caused boats to break free from their moorings. There are many reasons why a fitting may become loose, but one of the main factors is water seepage between the fitting and deck which causes the timber or laminate layers to rot. The bolts can, of course, also become loose – usually a result of too much strain being placed on the fitting. These problems can occur on older boats, so if you are looking for a second-hand model it is wise to check the security of such fittings by giving them a sharp tug with your hands or a little gentle prising with a small screwdriver.

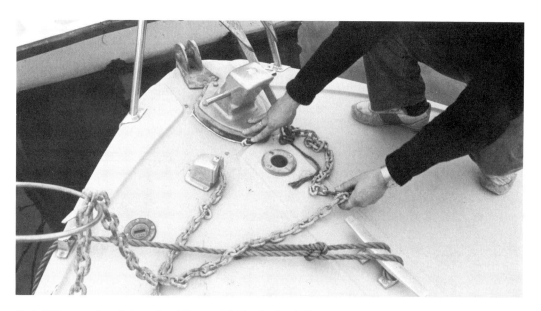

Deck fittings, anchor chains, pipe, fillers and fairleads should be given a good pull to ascertain their firmness. Check also for leaks below which could mean that the fitting may have to be removed and rebedded.

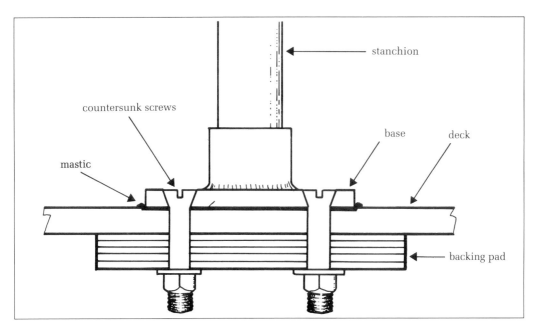

Deck fittings should all be secured through the deck to stout backing plates or timber pads. These provide extra support and spread the load in the area of the fitting as this may have to take extra strain.

Backing Plates

Load-bearing deck fittings such as cleats and bollards, which may have to take the strain of many pounds of pressure as ropes are tugged and pulled on tidal waters, should be bolted solidly through the deck to strong backing plates or pads. The bolt holes drilled for these fittings must be bedded down well on to a good-quality waterproof sealant. There are several types available, some of which are described later in this chapter, but the best come ready to use in a spring-loaded gun which makes application cleaner. A glass-fibre boat may have its deck strengthened by applying some extra layers of glass-fibre matting. Combining this with a large piece of sheet metal – say 5mm (¼in) in thickness – as a backing

One of the most vulnerable of all deck fittings is the sea-rail stanchion. These come in for a good deal of extra strain as people tend to grab them when boarding the boat or holding it into the side.

plate will give the cleat or winch all the support it needs.

On boats whose decks are built in layers with a central core, sometimes called a sandwich construction, do not overtighten the bolts on a fitting in case the applied pressure crushes the laminate, causing the deck to malform. Fitting metal collars around the bolts prior to putting them through the fitting and deck will bush them out, taking up any strain.

Fender eyes and small fittings such as canopy hooks are usually screwed straight down to the deck. Always re-member to ask for the correct type of screws when buying the fitting. Wood screws of the kind used in the domestic environment are useless and their threads will strip out as soon as you apply pressure from the screwdriver – this is especially true when screwing into glass fibre. Instead, always use stainless steel self-tapping screws and drill a small pilot hole first to allow the screw threads to get a grip. Generally, round-headed screws are better than countersunk ones. They not only look better on deck but are ideal in situations where the thickness of the deck and/or fitting is too shallow to allow a countersunk headed screw to be fitted.

Non-Slip Surfaces

Non-slip surfaces did not really come into their own until the advent of the glass-fibre deck. Before that there was really nothing to prevent your slipping over on the wet or icy surface of your boat, apart from a very good pair of rubber-soled shoes or boots. Even these did not always perform as they should, and so strained tendons, twisted arms and grazed knees if not more serious injuries often resulted. It is surprising just how slippery a surface can become when wet or icy, especially if it has a high-gloss paint coat or is very narrow (such as the gunwales on cruisers). A good deal of research has gone into the development of non-slip surfaces, and although most of this has been done for the benefit of industry the technology can easily be applied to boats. These surfaces, their application and effectiveness are discussed below.

Sand

Probably one of the first non-slip surfaces to be developed, and definitely the cheapest, is the sanded-paint surface. It is easier to apply to the deck area than some of the other surfaces because it can be made to cover awkward undulations in the surface of the deck, but in general it is messy and does tend to wear down quite quickly so that further back-up coats are required at the end of every season. Application is simple: the area to be covered is masked off with tape in the usual way and the paint is applied directly from the tin by brush. Remember to stir the paint well as when it dries the silver sand balls that make up the abras-ive surface always sink to the bottom of the tin.

If you are innovative and want to save some money, you can make up your own non-slip paint by adding silver sand (not beach or builder's sand) to gloss yacht enamel of the required colour. Remember to get the proportions right – about 0.5kg (1.1lb) of silver sand to 1 litre (1.8 pints) of paint – stir well and you are ready.

One other drawback with sanded paint is that it takes a very long time to dry. This

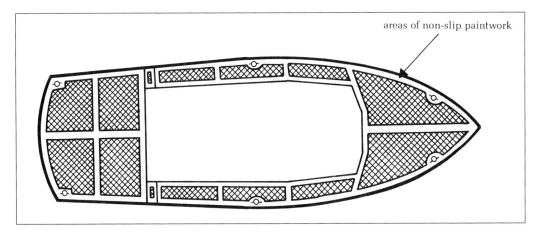

areas of non-slip paintwork

The deck of a boat can be masked off into zones before painting with non-slip paint or cutting in some Treadmaster or Trakmark non-slip material.

applies to paint you have made yourself as well as to commercial brands, and a good week should be left between painting and walking on the decks.

Moulded Surface

A method which is mainly confined to use on GRP boats is a pre-etched finish. This is built into the moulding of the superstructure of the boat at the appropriate points on side-decks, foredeck and cockpit. In my experience the etching never really goes deep enough to be effective, and this sort of surface is also prone to wear and tear as the polishing effect of countless pairs of shoes and boots takes the 'sharp' edges off the cross-hatched surface. It does look good as the areas etched can be controlled into patterns around the boat, but the long-term effectiveness soon calls this method into question.

If you own a cruiser with such a non-slip surface and it is wearing away, I find that a good way of repairing it is to go over

the area with a coat of the non-slip sanded paint mentioned above. Remember to clean off any dirt, grease or flaking paintwork before applying your paint.

Non-Slip Sheeting

Trakmark is a commercially made sheet covering material which serves two purposes: it has non-slip properties and can be used effectively on the decks and superstructure as a waterproofing covering. It is constructed of a flexible plastic which is bonded to a form of fabric cloth; it is very strong and is stuck down on the boat using contact adhesive. The material is bought by the foot off a roll at chandlers and is relatively easily cut to shape. The key point to remember is that you must prepare the surface of the deck well in advance, removing old paint, grease and oil to give good adhesion when sticking down the material.

In the early years of its life Trakmark has good non-slip properties and is very waterproof. It does, however, tend to be

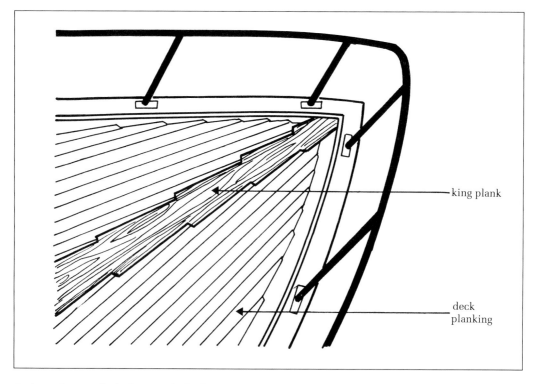

king plank

deck
planking

On larger boats teak planking can be laid on the deck. This looks very attractive and, as well as forming a good non-slip surface, can add to the insulation of the boat. Single planks can be used or you can buy fake planking in sheets!

damaged easily and will split and fade in its colour after several years in the open. After many years it will turn into a brittle state. It is, however, reasonably priced, easy to fit and, for those on a budget, it is an ideal covering outside or is excellent for use on cockpit floorboards, internal steps and cabin soles.

Treadmaster is another proprietary surface which is bought in sheets measuring slightly over 1m square. It is made of a synthetic, cork-like material and its deeply indented diamond pattern will be familiar to most boaters. In my opinion this is probably the best form of non-slip surface yet developed. Like the

Trakmark it is applied to the decks using a contact adhesive, but make sure you take the advice of the chandler and use the correct one as they are not all as effective as each other – using the wrong type can lead to the edges lifting after just a few months.

Treadmaster seems to be applied mainly as a covering on engines and on deck boards on boats where the edges are trimmed in angle aluminium to make a very neat job. As well as for deck work, the surface can be used on internal steps down to the cabin, on large areas of steel such as a boat roof, or (when cut into thin strips) down the gunwales. It has

Trakmark used as a non-slip surface on side decks and on these seats at the stern of a steel narrowboat.

A small strip of aluminium chequerplate screwed to the gunwale provides a non-slip step when boarding and disembarking.

excellent resistance to oil, petrol and water, and can be scrubbed down at the end of the season with soap and hot water. The only possible drawback might be the cost. When calculating how much you will need to complete the job, measure carefully in order to minimize waste and keep costs down.

Chequerplate

A surface which until recently was confined to the decks, gunwales and stern areas of steel boats – especially canal narrow boats – chequerplate is effective only in general terms and in dry weather, and may become ineffective as it becomes worn and shiny. You can now buy it in sheet aluminium form for use in engine rooms or cockpits, and it is simply cut to size using a hacksaw and looks very

attractive when in position. However, it is probably prohibitively expensive for all but the well-heeled boat owner.

Sealants

When wood was the only choice of boat-building material, the choice of sealants for caulking, bedding deck hatches and fittings was also strictly limited. White lead and putty formed the usual mixture for caulking planked hulls and this was applied after the caulking cotton had been hammered home along the length of each seam. It was also used for sealing cleats and bollards to the decks. Hot pitch poured into seams was another traditional material very widely used. These methods are still used today on traditional wooden boats by purists who may consider them to be far superior than the modern preparations.

Mastic

With the introduction of glass-fibre craft there was obviously a need for more compatible types of sealant, and today there is a choice to suit every need. The cheapest of the modern sealants, which is available from most builders' merchants and DIY shops, is the non-curing mastic. These very 'gooey' materials are ideal for bedding items which have a lot of movement. They generally form a skin after about twenty-four hours which is suitable for painting. Unfortunately, however, this skin is very thin and is easily punctured, thus exposing the underlying mastic. This can be messy if it gets on your clothes, but if left undisturbed the puncture will re-skin itself. Mastic is a very effective material for sealing items that are fully covered.

Silicone Rubber

Next in the price scale comes the silicone rubber sealants. These are also available from DIY shops as well as local yacht chandlers. They cure fully to a rubbery texture which has a fair amount of give when used on items that 'work' a lot – in other words, fittings that tend to flex slightly as the boat is used. The surfaces which are to be treated must be scrupulously clean, dry, and free from grease and oil to ensure good adhesion. It is possible to trim this type of sealant with a razor blade once cured, but I have found that doing this will often result in the seal being pulled away from the item which it is supposed to be sealing. It is far better to use masking tape along the edges that are

to be sealed, removing it before the sealant has had time to cure. This method gives a clean, straight edge to the work – especially useful when sealing around the edges of windows. Silicone rubber is available in a variety of colours, but black gives a very professional look when working on window frames.

Silicone rubber sealants are also excellent for making engine gaskets when the original gasket has been damaged or is not on board when emergency repairs are being undertaken. It can, however, have a corrosive effect on polypropylene fittings, so should not be used on items such as plastic-bodied navigation lights. Silicone-acrylics are a slightly cheaper form of silicone sealant. They have similar adhesive and sealing properties, and excess uncured sealant can be removed with water (none of the types of sealant mentioned so far are suitable for use under water).

Polysulphides

The best and most expensive sealant type currently available is the polysulphide, of which Life-Calk is the most commonly available example. It can take up to ten days to cure fully, but it can be applied in damp conditions and will cure more quickly if sprayed regularly with water. If a caulking job is undertaken between tides then this is the ideal sealing medium as the boat can be refloated immediately the job is complete and curing will take place while afloat! The use of polysulphide sealant on a traditional planked wooden craft in conjunction with correctly applied caulking cotton will result in a superior job to that accomplished with white lead and putty or a tar-pitch mixture. Another advantage of this sealant is that once it has cured fully it can be sanded to shape before painting takes place.

It has recently been discovered that polysulphide sealants can also affect polypropylene fittings. Certain types of sheet winch used on sailing craft are apparently particularly prone to these effects, although I have used this type of sealant on all sorts of jobs for several years and have never had any problems. To solve the problem of corroding on plastic items a new product called Life-Seal has recently been introduced for bedding down items on glass-fibre craft, both above and below the water-line. It also cures much faster than Life-Calk.

To sum up, if bedding deck fittings, windows and so on, especially on glass-fibre craft above the water-line, then use the silicone-rubber-type sealants. If working on a wooden craft, either bedding deck fittings or caulking the hull, use a poly-sulphide such as Life-Calk. For bedding underwater equipment such as through-hull transducers and skin fittings on glass-fibre, then use the polyurethane/silicone Life-Seal type of sealant.

Preparing the Surface

With any type of sealant a clean, dry surface is essential for good adhesion. All the different types of sealant are available in either small tubes or the much more economical cartridge sizes which are applied successfully and cleanly with a gun. These guns are very cheap and fit the many makes of sealant cartridge, all of which are a standard size.

If you are fairly adept at cake icing you will no doubt find these caulking guns very easy to use. The nozzle which is supplied with the cartridge is tapered, and this can be cut to give the desired size of sealant 'bead'. The sealant is squeezed from the gun and forced into the seam ahead of the nozzle, thus preventing air from being trapped in the seam. If the amount of sealant is judged correctly as you work along the seam then a clean job will be the result. However, if like me you tend to overapply the material then you will require a large supply of cleaning rags for removing the excess. I usually finish the job by smoothing off the surface with a damp finger, but if you have sensitive skin then this practice is best avoided.

Bow Propellers

Not many years ago the suggestion of fitting a bow thruster to a medium-sized seagoing motor cruiser to aid man-oeuvring in confined spaces would have been met with derision. But times and attitudes change, and as the market for bow thrusters on large luxury cruisers increases so there is now an increase in interest from owners of smaller craft.

A bow thruster suitable for medium-sized as well as large cruisers is the Vetus Bow Propeller, and this is the unit which is used as the example below. The Vetus unit is a specially designed sealed-down version of the type of thruster used on large ships for manoeuvring in confined harbours, and consists of a reversible DC electric motor of either 12 or 24 volts. It has a rated output of 3 kilowatts and drives a 7-inch three-bladed propeller via a bevel gear train in an oil bath at 3,400rpm. It is recommended that a separate battery should be provided for the sole use of the bow propeller, and that

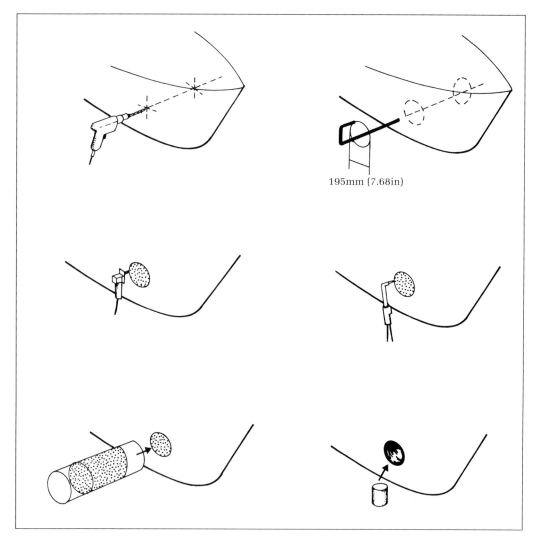

195mm (7.68in)

The various stages involved in fitting a bow propeller to a boat. The holes are drilled and cut using either a jig-saw for GRP or a steel cutter on a steel hull. The tunnel tube is inserted and sealed into position before fitting the prop itself.

it should be mounted in the same compartment so as to keep voltage drop to a minimum – the current drawn is around 250 amps, although only for very short bursts.

The propeller is mounted in a tunnel, which is installed across the boat near to the bow, and can be supplied in GRP, aluminium or steel to suit the construction material of the boat. The propeller fits snugly in the tube, having minimal clearance between the blade tips and the installations will be required in older boats, and in this case the area in the bow of the boat must be inspected to ensure that there is sufficient room for the tunnel and the electric motor unit before work can commence. The design allows for the motor to be installed in a variety of positions around the centre of the tunnel. The standard position is above the tunnel directly over the propeller, but if there is insufficient headroom the motor can be placed horizontally forward or aft of the tube, or at any convenient angle in between. In some boats it may prove uneconomical to fit a bow prop due to the large amount of alterations which may be required.

If the preparations for fitting to an older boat are not complicated, or if the unit is to be installed into a new boat, then the work required is well within the scope of the keen DIY owner. If the unit is to be fitted in a GRP boat then the tunnel is obviously bonded in with mat and resin, but for steel or aluminium craft the tunnel is welded into place. The provision of a weed hatch over the propeller is a worthwhile and simple addition to make during building. Weld an additional length of tube at right angles to the main cross tube and to a height which gives safe clearance above the water-line so that in the event of rubbish being drawn into the tunnel and fouling the prop it can be removed easily and quickly.

The minimum depth to the centre of the propeller from the water-line to ensure that air is not drawn down into the prop is 23cm (9in), so this dimension must be taken into account when planning the installation. The centre point of the tunnel should be marked carefully on each side of the hull and then checked to ensure that both marks are in exactly the

The neat bow propeller unit from Vetus. The motor unit can be seen atop with the left/right control panel to the right. The sealing flange which separates the motor from the propeller through the hull of the boat can be seen above the propeller itself.

tunnel wall. This gives the unit some of the characteristics of a water jet by concentrating the thrust in a confined direction – either to port or starboard of the bow depending on the direction selected on the operating control.

Fitting

It is obviously a very much simpler task to build in the tunnel during construction of the boat, at which point surrounding equipment, tanks and plumbing can be designed around the unit, and wiring for the electric motor can be routed through the boat in specially prepared ducting. However, it is also very likely that same position, port and starboard. A hole should then be drilled at each centre mark and a simple prefabricated marker inserted right through with which to scribe the hole size for cutting out the tunnel apertures. A piece of stiff rod with a chalk marker fixed to it will do the job and will ensure that even if there is a marked taper to the hull sides the cutting marks will still give a perfect shape for tunnel fitting.

Boats with bluff bows will generally be fairly beamy, so it is sound practice to weld in supports below the tunnel for additional stiffness. Deflectors on the outside of each tunnel aperture help to keep rubbish from entering, and on steel boats these are simply welded on as part of the fitting process.

Once the tunnel is installed it should be protected against corrosion with the same paint scheme as is used for the rest of the boat before the propeller and motor unit are installed. The instructions are very comprehensive for the latter and involve nothing more complex than accurately drilling three holes using the template provided. The position of these three holes decides the alignment of the propeller in the tunnel, and so they need to be perfectly aligned with the centre line of the tunnel. Once the holes have been drilled the installation procedure can be followed, ensuring that gaskets and sealant are fitted in the correct order. The oil reservoir is then connected to the drive unit via the 8mm hose provided, and fixed in a position at least 50cm (20in) above the water-line, although this dimension could probably be reduced a little for inland craft.

Electrics

The electrical system needs careful attention to ensure that the unit operates properly. The first requirement is for good ventilation to the area around the motor and its battery to ensure adequate cooling of the motor and the removal of any gases given off by the battery during charging. Having a separate battery means that a diode charge-splitter is also required to ensure that the battery is charged properly and that it cannot draw current from the engine-starting or domestic battery. The main power feed cables need to be of very heavy cross section, again to keep voltage drop to a minimum – for long runs of over 10m (30ft) cable of at least 70mm sq (7½in sq) in cross-section will be required. This is about the same size used for heavy engine starter cable or welding cable and must have properly soldered end fittings. Once these important requirements are met, the rest of the installation is very straightforward as comprehensive instructions are always provided by the manufacturer.

Using the Bow Prop

The control for the bow prop is in the form of a joystick which gives thrust to either port or starboard. An on-off switch is provided and a green warning light indicates when the unit is switched on and ready for use. The maximum running time is five minutes in every ten to allow the unit time to cool down, but as the prop is usually used only in short bursts this time is more than adequate for all normal uses.

Conditions where these units will prove most useful is when a wind is blowing across a crowded marina, making manoeuvring difficult in the confined space available. The bow propeller can be

Fenders are a very important part of the boat's external protection. But it is useless having a new fender if it is attached to the boat by a bit of string as shown here.

used to move the bows away from the pontoon and make tight turns in crowded marinas very much easier. In fact, this is one of those pieces of equipment which, once installed, makes you wonder how you ever managed without it.

Anchor Winches

On smaller craft an anchor windlass is not an essential part of the deck equipment as the anchor and chain (or rope) are generally light enough to be handled easily. However, on larger craft with heavy ground tackle and large amounts of chain it becomes much more important.

The choice of whether to opt for a manual model or a power model – either electric or hydraulic – is largely a question of finance and also how often the anchor will be used. Many people

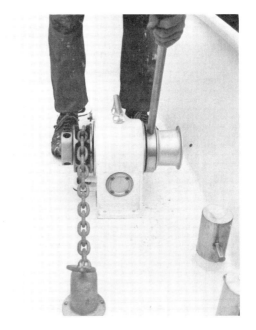

The anchor winch in its manual mode. A bar is inserted to enable the chain to be winched aboard or let out slowly.

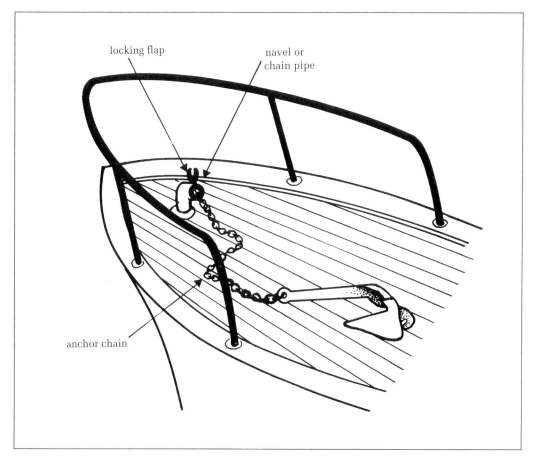

locking flap

navel or chain pipe

anchor chain

The chain pipe allows the anchor chain to flow freely when the anchor is being raised or lowered.
The small flap can be slipped over a link of chain to lock it into position.

never use their anchors, instead cruising from marina to marina and keeping their ground tackle solely for emergencies – there are even people who stupidly cruise tidal estuaries and rivers with no anchor at all! If you enjoy the seclusion of quiet bays and backwaters, and like to spend some of your time away from the hubbub of marinas then reliable ground tackle is essential, and for ease of use an anchor windlass is a very good idea.

My personal preference is for an electric model which gives the additional facility of dropping and weighing anchor single-handed from the helm position if necessary. It is pointless selecting a windlass that is too large for the job as it will only take up valuable space on the foredeck and may make electrical demands that your batteries cannot cope with. Unless the winch is installed correctly with due regard to secure mounting, alignment with the chain pipe or bow roller, and good electrical practice it

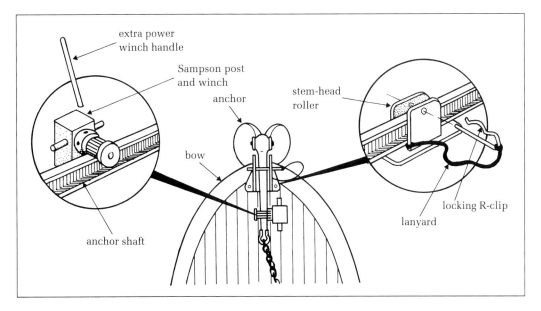

extra power
winch handle

Sampson post
and winch

anchor

stem-head
roller

bow

locking R-clip

lanyard

anchor shaft

Manual anchor winches can include a steel bar which will allow easy hauling. The anchor can be stowed safely on deck and prevented from moving around in heavy seas by fitting a small locking clip on a lanyard.

can become a nightmare to operate and can even endanger the craft upon which it is installed.

Chain Locker

The first consideration is the chain locker. This should be a sealed compartment as low down in the bows of the vessel as possible, thereby ensuring that the weight of the chain carries itself down into the locker and away from the windlass. There should also be sufficient space in the locker for the chain to pile up on itself without blocking the chain pipe. If this occurs, the chain will be prevented from leaving the gypsy and will pile up on deck, eventually jamming the windlass and leaving you with a partially raised anchor which may be swinging around just below the water-line and causing

The chain pipe at deck level showing the anchor chain held fast by the special notched plate.

untold damage. Getting the chain locker arrangement absolutely right is probably the most important part of windlass installation, and although it may require a fair bit of work this will all be worth while when the anchor chain is running smoothly.

Mounting the Windlass

The next consideration is the mounting of the windlass. It should be borne in mind that most electrically driven anchor windlasses have a pulling capacity of almost half a tonne or more when under full load, and if the mounting is not strong enough it could conceivably tear itself out of the deck. I must admit that I have never heard of such an instance, but it is as well to bear the power of these units in mind.

On boats I have owned I always opted for stowing the anchor outboard of the starboard bow – 'big ship style' – which entails fitting a hawse pipe from the deck to the bow side. To keep the foredeck uncluttered, the windlass can be installed to one side but individual preference and differing deck layouts will usually dictate the mounting position. A standard galvanized chain pipe is mounted on top of the hawse pipe which directs the chain on to the gypsy. The chain-locker pipe is directly beneath the windlass and a chain stripper incorporated in the windlass design ensures the chain fits easily into the pipe. Plastic hose can be used as a chain-locker pipe and prevents any rattling of the chain at night which would otherwise disturb occupants in the fore-cabin.

The chain locker itself should be glassed out with two layers of medium-weight mat and resin to protect the hull interior from chipping as the chain runs

in or out, and also to seal in any odours of weed which may have been brought aboard. It is also an effective way of ensuring watertightness between the hull, locker bulkhead and the bottom of the locker, the latter being concrete to make a flat surface on which the chain lies. A drainpipe and valve should also be included to allow the locker to be drained periodically if necessary.

Fitting the Unit

Fitting the windlass is quite straightforward as it is bolted to the deck using stainless steel nuts and bolts through 1cm (⅜in) steel backing pads to help spread the load. Before bolting down, the electrical cables are run up through a hole in the deck and into a corresponding hole in the bottom of the windlass, which means that no cables are showing on deck and the installation looks neat. With the motor cover removed, the cables can be passed through the windlass body ready for connection later on. The windlass can then be bolted down on to a hardwood pad if desired, using generous amounts of sealant which should preferably be cleaned off before it sets.

Electrical Connections

The electrical installation is critical to good performance and the first requirement is to ensure that cables are of sufficient size to take the load – around 300 amps for a powerful unit under full power. For this reason it is essential that you use cables of heavy cross-section such as those used for diesel engine starting, and the longer the run of cable the larger the cross-sectional area should be.

Electrical connections to the anchor winch. Note the sizeable cross-section of the cables used.

The heavy-duty relay that must be fitted into the winch's electrical circuitry.

It is possible to install a battery near the winch to act as its own power supply, and it is then only necessary to run cables capable of taking charge current. If this method is used then very careful design of the charge circuit is essential to prevent the windlass from drawing power from other on-board batteries through the charge circuit (which would be unable to take the load and could easily result in a fire). For this reason it is better to accept some voltage drop on a long run for the sake of safety.

To operate such a heavy current, a relay in the circuit is required. These are usually available from the supplier of the winch and come in two common types. One such relay is a simple on-off unit for hauling only and comes complete with one operating button, but you can use a reversible model which allows both hauling (bringing in) and veering (letting down) of the chain. This means that it is possible to drop anchor without leaving the helm position, a feature which can be very helpful in certain situations.

Wiring of the relay is simple, with two heavy cables – positive and negative – running from the battery to the remote relay and then on to the windlass, with a light wire from each control button to one terminal on each side of the relay and an earth to the operating side of the relay. Depending on which button is pressed, the relay will reverse the polarity to the windlass to give either forward or reverse running. Incidentally, if both buttons are pressed simultaneously nothing will happen as the relay is off when both buttons are in the same position. This means that the system is fail-safe. Having the relay built into the system means that it is possible to operate the windlass from as many locations as you care to fit switches or buttons.

Operating the Windlass

To drop the anchor it is first necessary to free the locking clip on the top of the gypsy, after which a handle is inserted in one of the holes in the side of the gypsy clutch. By moving the handle a short distance in an anticlockwise direction to release the cone clutch, the chain will run out. The speed of letting go can be controlled with the handle simply by tightening the clutch slightly. When the required amount of chain for the depth of water has run out the clutch is locked in, again using the handle. This is the usual method of letting go and ensures that the chain runs out quickly, although care must be taken to ensure that the chain

The scene below decks of the chain pipe through which the anchor chain passes from the deck to the chain locker at the bow. This arrangement is standard on many production boats.

The anchor is stowed neatly at the bow and is ready for immediate use. Stowing an anchor in this way looks much tidier than leaving it on the foredeck, and with a winch fitted it will always be ready for use.

does not run out so far as to pile on top of the anchor and prevent it digging in. The other method of letting go, which has already been mentioned, is to run the chain out electrically after releasing the locking clip, although the chain will run out much more slowly using this method.

Once the anchor has dug in and the correct amount of chain is out, a bridle should be used to take the weight off the gypsy. A cleat is mounted on top of the windlass for this purpose and also makes a handy mooring point. The bridle can consist of a short piece of chain or rope with a quick-release hook in one end which is attached to the anchor chain, and with a loop in the other end which drops over the cleat on the windlass. The gypsy clutch is then released and the strain is taken on the cleat. The same

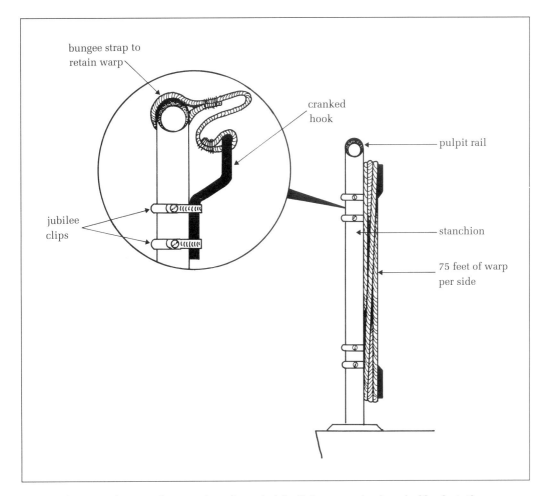

bungee strap to retain warp

cranked hook

pulpit rail

jubilee clips

stanchion

75 feet of warp per side

Ropes and mooring lines can be stowed neatly on deck by fitting a couple of cranked hooks to the sea-rail stanchions. The ropes are wound around the hooks and are secured by a rubber bungee cord.

function can be performed with a pin placed through a link of the chain and through holes in the bow roller. If you are anchored in calm weather or only stopping for lunch then the use of a bridle will not usually be necessary.

Before weighing anchor it is essential to have your engines running as the current consumed by the windlass is so great that it could possibly leave you with insufficient starting power! It is normal practice to have the engines running before weighing anchor anyway, so this should not be a problem. I should emphasize that the high current consumption quoted is only used during breaking out of the anchor, as once it is free the windlass is lifting only the weight of the anchor and chain, and consumption may be as low as 30–40 amps. Once the anchor is fully home it should be secured using the bridle to prevent it accidentally running out when under way.

Safety

Great care must always be taken when using an anchor windlass, and young children should not be allowed anywhere near it when it is operational. Although it is only a small piece of equipment, the reserves of power are large and a finger trapped in the chain could easily be lost.

Should there be insufficient battery power available to operate the windlass then it is possible to operate it manually using the handle provided for letting go the gypsy clutch. It is simply inserted in the holes on the drum side of the windlass and operated in the manner of a manual winch through a ratchet built into the unit. This method could also be used in the case of a fouled anchor to help preserve battery power, and really gives you the best of both worlds – manual and electric.

SUMMARY

- Loose or broken cleats, fairleads and rigging anchor points can be dangerous, causing boats to break free of their moorings and equipment to fail – usually at the most inconvenient of times.

- If you are innovative and want to save some money, you can make up your own non-slip paint by adding silver sand (not beach or builder's sand) to gloss yacht enamel of the required colour.

- When using sealant to bed down fittings or to seal windows, use masking tape along the edges that are to be sealed, removing it before the sealant has had time to cure. This method gives a clean, straight edge to the work – especially useful when sealing around the edges of windows.

- In some boats it may prove uneconomical to fit a bow prop due to the large amount of alterations which may be required. Check the size and construction of your craft first.

- Great care must always be taken when using an anchor windlass, and young children should not be allowed anywhere near it when it is operational.

11
FITTING A TOW BRACKET TO YOUR CAR

Being able to tow your boat behind your car in order to reach different crusing areas is a great way of extending the use and season of your craft. However, if you are to take advantage of this activity you will need to fulfil two main criteria first: the boat must be within the legal weight and size limits for towing; and your car must be powerful enough for the job without straining the engine or placing excessive wear and tear on its fabric. If you are thinking about trailing a boat, find out first just what weight your car will legally tow. You can always ask your local car dealer who should have all the figures to hand.

Your next decision concerns the type of bracket you wish to fit. There are several available on the market but some are of dubious reputation. Choose from a reputable supplier or sales outlet such as a chain of motoring accessory shops that operate countrywide. In this way you can be relatively certain that the bracket and wiring kit you buy will be of a good standard. The procedure for fitting is simple enough, the only tools required being an electric drill, spanners to fit the bolts, a tape measure and a pencil.

Fitting Procedure

The first thing to do is to remove the trim from the boot, along with the spare wheel, jack and spanner. Then take off the rear bumper as the bracket's main mounting point is hidden just behind it. This is done with little fuss – on the car I use in this example, a Vauxhall Cavalier, it is just a matter of loosening two bolts in the boot and sliding the bumper away from the side brackets.

Next, measure accurately the centre of the car – this is important as the towing ball must be positioned centrally for correct towing and so that it complies with the law. On the Cavalier a protruding strip on the rear valance is the correct place, and four bolt holes can be marked off using part of the bracket as a template. Now comes the next bit – drilling holes in the car! Use a smaller drill bit than is actually required to create four pilot holes in the correct positions. Enlarge these with the correct size of drill and recheck that your efforts are still aligned with the holes on the bracket.

The towing ball is then fitted to the upper part of the bracket and bolted

The component parts of the average towing bracket assembly laid out before fitting to the car.

loosely to the car. The instructions state that no bolt should be tightened home fully until the whole bracket has been fitted roughly in place. This saves distortion from occurring and also makes for easy alignment.

There are one or two things which have to be purchased in addition to the bracket: a towing ball, a lighting socket, a mounting plate, a cable and connectors. The fitting of the electrics is dealt with in the next section, but the socket plate and tow ball have to be incorporated at this stage. The final part of the bracket is the long extension bar which provides support underneath the car. This is attached loosely to the upper bracket and held in place under the spare-wheel pan. Holes are drilled through in the same way as before and the bar is bolted into position using the bolts supplied. It helps when

tightening if one person gets into the boot to hold a socket on the head of the bolt while another tightens the nut from below. Once this has been done it is a simple matter of tightening all bolts and making sure that the bracket is rigid and secure.

Electrics

The first thing to do before attempting any work on the car's wiring is to disconnect the main battery. You need to wire the towing bracket so that when the boat or caravan trailer is plugged into the socket at the tow ball the trailer indicators, stop and tail lights work in unison with those of the car. You can purchase a complete kit for this job (*see* the table opposite). The one used in the example is a type which includes a special flasher relay

STANDARD ELECTRICS KIT

The standard electrics kit available to allow the trailer and car lights to work in unison will contain the following:

Socket mounting bracket
Seven-pin socket with cover
Seven-core cable
Special splicing connectors
Flasher relay
Fuse
Warning lamp
Double-sided tape

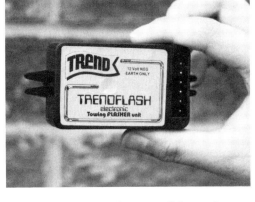

A special heavy-duty relay unit will have to be fitted if your car is not already wired for towing.

which makes the system more powerful. If you rely on the car flasher system to work both the car and trailer indicators you can overload the system so that neither works efficiently, if at all. If you are buying the items separately make sure that you purchase the correct type of socket, this being a 12N or normal socket. A warning light must also be fitted to the dashboard of the car to indicate to the driver that the lights on the trailer are actually flashing with those of the car.

Before you start, check the earthing of your car as most heavy-duty relay flashers will operate only from negative earth vehicles. Once this has been done, you can set about wiring up the socket which is attached to the bracket and bolted through to the tow bar via the ball hitch unit. The international code for the seven-core cable is given in the table below. If the socket you have bought is not pre-wired, strip off about 5cm (2in) of the insulation from one end of the wire and about ½ cm (¼in) from the insulation on each of the seven internal coloured wires. Carefully connect each wire to its appropriate terminal.

SEVEN-CORE CABLE CODE

Yellow Left-hand indicator
Blue Spare or rear fog light
White Earth
Green Right-hand indicator
Brown Right-hand sidelight
Red Brake lights
Black Left-hand sidelight

The next job is to reassemble the socket and to feed the seven-core cable through the sealing grommet before attaching the socket assembly to the tow ball hitch. Locate the socket on its thin metal bracket with the hinge uppermost and fit with the screws provided.

The seven-core cable must then be taken into the boot of the vehicle. If no convenient hole exists, drill a 1cm (½in) hole behind the bumper as near to the centre as possible, fitting the grommet to prevent chafing and leakage of water. Feed the cable through the grommet into the boot and pull gently to take up the slack.

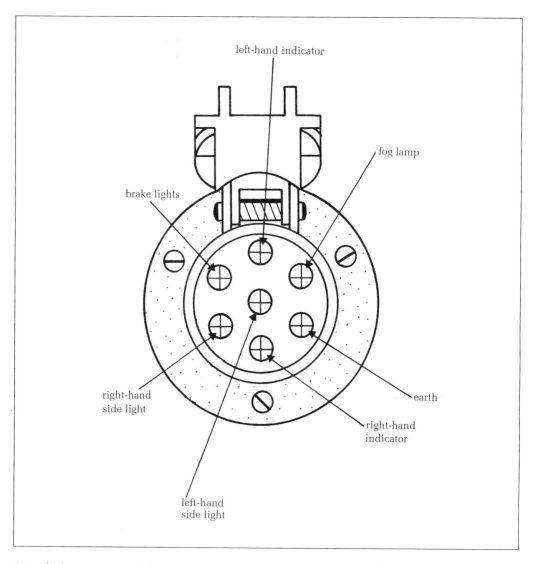

A standard seven-pin tow ball socket assembly showing standard wiring configuration.

Next, you must locate the wiring loom which supplies power to the lights. Once found, select a suitable point at which to splice in the new connections. Trace the wire on the car leading to the brake lights and splice the red cable from the socket into it using a splicing connector. Do the same thing with the left- and right-hand sidelights using a splicing coupler on the black and brown wires respectively. Fit a ring connector to the white wire and attach it with a bolt and nut to earth. Scrape away any paint if necessary to achieve a good earthing.

Fit the one end of the seven-core cable into the correct terminals on the lighting socket.

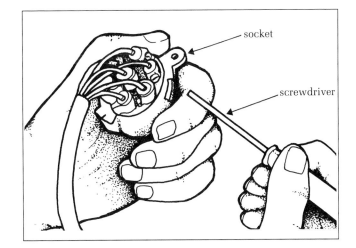

Fit the socket assembly to the car tow ball using the special bracket provided in the kit.

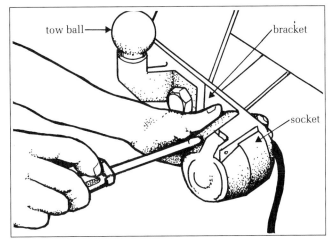

A hole is drilled through the bottom of the boot of the car near to the rear-light wiring cable loom.

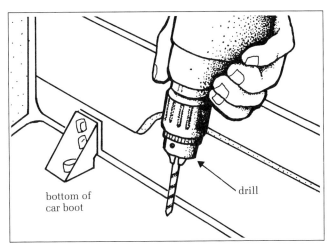

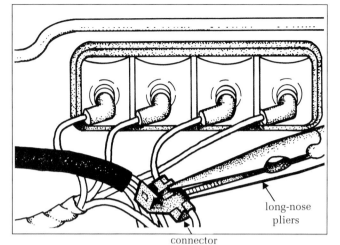

connector

long-nose
pliers

Using the instructions in your kit, connect each cable to the lighting cables using the special no-cut connectors.

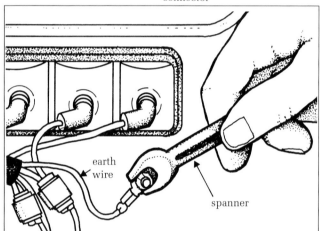

earth
wire

spanner

Choose a suitable point to attach the white earth cable, making sure that you have a good electrical connection. Scrape away any paint if necessary.

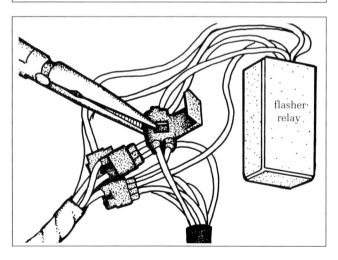

flasher
relay

Splice in the heavy-duty flasher control relay, again using the instructions supplied with your particular device.

Fit the in-line fuse and fuseholder.

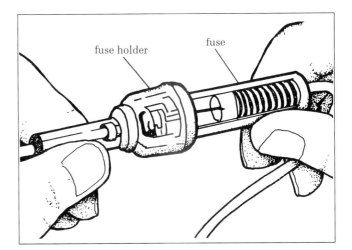

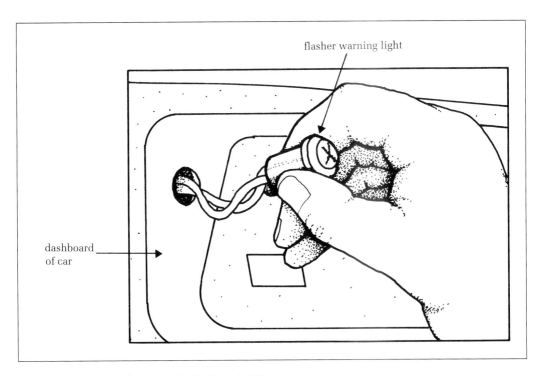

Fit the flasher warning light into the dashboard of the car.

The special seven-pin electrical socket fitted to its metal plate and ready to be bolted on to the towing bracket.

Find a suitable position in the boot to which you can fix the relay unit and stick it into position using the double-sided tape supplied. Connect the yellow and green wires coming from the relay unit to the yellow and green wires on the seven-core cable, then refer to the instructions to couple up the other two wires to the left- and right-hand indicators. Wire up the relay for power using the boot light switch or another suitable supply, then fit an in-line fuseholder and fuse to protect the circuit.

Finally, run the remaining relay flasher lead to the dashboard of the car and choose a suitable place in which to fit the warning-lamp holder. Connect the wire from the relay to one side of the lamp and run a short lead to earth from the other. Check all the wiring and ensure that connections are well made. Your trailing socket is now wired up and ready to accept the boat trailer.

SUMMARY

- If you are thinking about trailing a boat, find out first just what weight your car will legally tow. You can always ask your local car dealer who should have all the figures to hand.

- Choose your towing bracket from a reputable supplier or sales outlet such as a chain of motoring accessory shops that operate countrywide. In this way you can be relatively certain that the bracket and wiring kit you buy will be of a good standard.

- The first thing to do before attempting any work on the car's wiring is to disconnect the main battery.

- A warning light must be fitted to the dashboard of the car to indicate to the driver that the lights on the trailer are actually flashing with those of the car.

GLOSSARY

Abaft: Behind.

Abeam: At one side of the centre section of the boat.

Adrift: A boat or item that is loose or unmoored.

Aft: The back of the boat.

Ahead: In the front part of the boat.

Amidships: In the centre of the boat.

Astern: Behind the boat, reverse and so on.

Athwartships: Across the boat.

Awash: At the same level as the water.

Ballast: Weight placed in the lower part of a boat to give stability and trim.

Bar: A shallow spit of sand or mud across a harbour entrance.

Beam: Width of the boat, usually measured from a central position.

Bear off: Move off from a quayside mooring.

Belay: Securing a warp or rope around a cleat, bollard and the like.

Below: Inside the cabin of the boat.

Bight: A loop in the centre section of a rope.

Bilge: The bottom of the boat's interior.

Bitter end: The last link in the anchor chain.

Boat hook: A pole or staff with a hook at one end.

Bollard: Stout mooring post.

Bow: The front of a boat.

Broach: The boat swings quickly side-on to the oncoming waves.

Bulkhead: An internal partition separating cabins and so on.

Bulwarks: A low, solid railing around the deck area.

Buoy: A floating navigation mark.

Casting off: Letting go a mooring rope.

Cleat: A special deck fitting to which ropes can be tied off and secured.

Coaming: The raised section surrounding the cockpit.

Cockpit: The area (usually at the stern) in which the crew sits to control the boat.

Deck: The walkable surface above decks.

Dinghy: A small, open craft used on larger boats as a tender.

Displacement: Total weight of the boat.

Draft: The amount of the boat that sits below the water-line.

Fairlead: A special fitting at deck level into which the mooring ropes are guided.

Fairway: The unencumbered, navigable channel.

Fathom: A unit of measurement equivalent to 6 feet.

Fender: Plastic air-filled bags used to protect the sides of a vessel.

Fiddle rail: Bolt-on attachment to the cooker to stop pans from sliding off the rings.

Flake: To lay the anchor rope or chain in a loose figure of eight on deck.

Flukes: The pointed parts of an anchor.

Freeboard: The amount of measurable deck above the water-line.

Galley: The cooking area aboard a boat.

Gimbals: A swinging pivot which keeps the cooker, compass *et al* upright at all times.

Ground tackle: The anchor and its associated warps and chain.

Gunwale: The joint between the topsides and the deck.

Heads: The name for the boat's toilet facility.

Helm: The steering position.

Helmsman: The person steering the boat at the tiller or wheel.

Holding ground: The type of seabed (mud, shale, rock and so on) used when anchoring.

Inboard: The area inside or on the boat.

Jury rig: A rudder, mast or similar made from other parts of the boat in an emergency.

Keel: The spine of the boat or the weighted section under the hull.

Knot: A unit of speed equivalent to 1 nautical mile per hour.

Lee side: The side of the boat opposite the wind.

Leeward: Away from the direction of the wind.

Leeway: The sideways drift of the boat caused by the action of the wind.

Life-jacket: A safety device that keeps a person afloat.

Log: An electrical or mechanical device used to measure the boat's speed and distance through the water.

Logbook: A record kept aboard of navigational details of a voyage.

Make fast: Securing a warp to a cleat or bollard.

Mooring: Tying up alongside or to a swinging buoy.

Nautical mile: A unit of measurement equal to approximately 2,000 yards.

Outboard: Outside the boat; portable petrol-driven propulsion unit.

Overfalls: A confused area of water where two tidal systems meet.

Painter: A mooring rope for a small dinghy or tender.

Port: The left-hand side of a boat when facing forward.

Pulpit: The guard-rail that surrounds the bow area.

Pushpit: The guard-rail that surrounds the stern area.

Quarter: The rear corner of a boat.

Riding light: The white anchor light.

Rowlock: A swivel bracket on the gunwale of a rowing boat in which the oar is held.

Rubbing strake: Timber, plastic or rubber fendering in a strip to protect the sides of a boat.

Rudder: A flat blade which swivels underwater at the sten and which is used for steering the boat.

Scuppers: Drain holes low down in the bulwarks.

Seizing: A lashing joint that holds two warps together.

Set of tide: The direction in which the tide runs.

Shackle: A metal fitting with a screw gate.
Shank: The long arm of an anchor.
Sheer: To swing about the anchor.
Shoal water: Very shallow, fast-running water.
Slack water: The period at which there is no measurable tidal flow.
Sounding: The depth of water shown on the chart.
Spring: An extra one or two mooring lines that prevent fore and aft movement on a quayside.
Stanchion: A stout post supporting the sea railing.
Starboard: The right-hand side of the boat when facing forward.
Steerage way: Sufficient speed to allow the rudder to alter the boat's course.
Stem: The front of the bow.
Stern: The back part of the boat.

Tender: A small boat carried aboard and used for getting ashore.

Thwart: A small wooden or plastic seat in the tender or dinghy.
Tiller: The long shaft of wood or metal connected to the rudder and used for steering.
Topsides: The section of the boat above the water-line.
Transducer: A device used to relay and emit echo signals for soundings.

Underway: The boat, when moving through the water unattached.
Up and down: When the anchor warp is in a vertical attitude.

Wake: The trail of foam and wavelets left astern of a moving boat.
Warp: A term for a rope or line.
Watch: A period of time that a person spends steering or navigating.
Wind rode: The boat when lying to wind at anchor.

Yaw: To wander either side of a predetermined course.

INDEX